Herbalism Through the Ages

Herbalism Through the Ages

by

RALPH WHITESIDE KERR

ROSICRUCIAN LIBRARY
VOLUME XXX

SUPREME GRAND LODGE OF AMORC, INC.
Printing and Publishing Department
San Jose, California

First Edition, 1969

Library of Congress Catalog Card Number: 74-96813
ISBN 0-912057-24-6

4-87

Seventh Edition, 1980
Second Printing, 1983

BF
1623
.R7
R65
v.30
c.1

Contents

The Rosicrucian Library

Volume

(Other volumes will be added from time to time.
Write for complete catalogue.)

Foreword

TRADITION, FOLKLORE, LITERATURE, HISTORY, SCI-
ence, and the arts all play a vital part in the study of herbs. I
first became intensely interested in Herbalism years ago, when
I was doing my University Postgraduate work at the University of Montana. One of the courses was Research Work in
Systematic Botany. The basic text and reference work was
Rydberg's *Flora of the Rocky Mountain States and Adjacent
Plains.* Combined with this fascinating field work in Nature's
laboratory was a consideration of Plant and Animal Ecology—
how plants affect each other and the mutual influence of plants
and animals, including man.

In the very beginning of the human race, we find the Bible
reference: "And God said, 'Behold, I have given you every herb
bearing seed, that is upon the face of the earth.'" (Genesis
1:29) Herbs have been an integral part of all life, human,
animal, and vegetable, since time began.

Much of the material covered by this book is the result of
knowledge gained through the years since 1925, when I first
became deeply interested in the study of Herbs, in my University work. In addition to study, this included much research
work and experimentation. Some of the references read or consulted are listed:

For accurate, systematic Botanical knowledge, Rydberg's
monumental work mentioned above is recommended. For Historical and Traditional information, study Dioscorides of

Ancient Greece; Culpepper (1653); John Gerrard, London, 1597; William Coles, 1657; Funk & Wagnalls' New Standard Encyclopedia; The Encyclopaedia Britannica; the writings of Pliny; and FLORA (1799—Author unknown). Other references included FOLKLORE AND ODYSSEY OF FOOD AND MEDICINAL PLANTS, by the Lehners: HERBS AND THE FRAGRANT GARDEN, by Brownlow; STALKING THE HEALTHFUL HERBS, by Euell Gibbons; HERBS, by Dorothy Childs Hogner; HERBS, by Webster; PLANT DRUGS THAT CHANGED THE WORLD, by Norman Taylor; ALL THE PLANTS OF THE BIBLE, by Walker; HERBAL, by Krutch; THE SCIENCE AND ART OF PERFUMERY, by Sagarin; THE FRAGRANT PATH, by Louise Beebee Wilder; SEEDS AND SPROUTS FOR LIFE and other books by Dr. Bernard Jensen of Hidden Valley Health Ranch, Lake Wohlford, R.F.D. #4, Escondido, California. Our gratitude goes to Dr. Jensen for many courtesies afforded during frequent visits, observations, and researches at Hidden Valley, where Herbalism reigns supreme.

In every instance where a direct quotation has been made from any published work, permission has been secured and grateful acknowledgment is made. We are especially thankful for the outstanding, valuable research work and excellent suggestions by Miss Muriel Daniels, of Oakdale, Long Island, New York. Gratitude is also expressed to the staff of the Escondido Public Library for their cooperation and encouragement.

RALPH WHITESIDE KERR

8

PART ONE

LEGEND, ANTIQUITY, AND EARLY HISTORY

CHAPTER ONE

From the Dawn of Civilization

THE STORY OF HERBS IS ANYTHING BUT A SIMPLE one. It involves an excursion into the realm of evolution. It considers the changing factors that influenced the development of religious practices in various nations of the world. It is linked with problems in mythology and history. It may be said to be the forerunner of the modern sciences of medicine and chemistry, particularly organic chemistry. An understanding of Nature's Alchemy derived from a study of herbs and herbal products leads us into a keener appreciation of aesthetic influences in anthropology.

Mysticism is a striving to learn and understand the nature and operation of the primal cause, the Universal Mind, the Creative Power of which all humanity is an integral part. The study of herbs and herbal products furnishes an entry into knowledge that is interrelated, demonstrating the universality of creation. As the Philosopher Hegel has stated, "All knowledge is one. If we can know everything about any one thing, we will know all."

The dictionary defines an herb as "A seed plant devoid of woody tissue which dies completely or to the ground

11

after flowering; an herbaceous plant valued for medicinal properties or for its sweet smell or taste."

Even before the dawn of history, artifacts and other evidences discovered by archeologists and researchers prove that herbs and herbal products played an important part in the individual and communal life of the human beings who were developing the use of the God-given characteristic of creativity.

From legends and the earliest records, we learn that herbs and herbal products were used as incense. Sweet-smelling substances were burned to please or appease the gods, under the direction of the ancient priests, whose power, in many instances, surpassed even that of the leaders of the tribes. Their increasing awareness soon convinced them that the herbal products from which incense was made possessed curative powers as well as pleasing aromas and the priests became "medicine men" as well as religious leaders of the people. From this primitive beginning the modern science of healing developed.

Probably the most ancient authentic records that exist regarding the use of herbs, herbal products, and related materials, as incense, for medicinal purposes and for perfume essences have been discovered in the hieroglyphic records in royal tombs and temples on the west bank of the Nile River near the site of the ancient city of Thebes, in Egypt. It has been estimated that these tombs were constructed several thousand years before the Christian Era. In these records, honey is mentioned as a food and for its curative properties.

12

This knowledge regarding the use of herbs and herbal products in various ways as related in the temple and tomb records of the country of the Pharaohs did not come into being spontaneously at this particular time. It is logical to conclude, then, that the established practice and application of the many properties of the herbs and their derivatives, which may be termed herbal products, can trace their beginnings, through legend and folklore, into many lands, since the development and dawn of civilization.

An understanding of this will emphasize the realization that the study of Herbalism is truly an excursion into the field of Nature's Alchemy.

From legendary times, long before the earliest records can be regarded as historical, very few artifacts have been discovered that indicate the development of aesthetic emotions among the representatives of *Homo sapiens.* Neanderthal Man and his predecessors probably were too busy defending themselves against natural enemies to think of anything except brute force against the hazards of existence. In the drawings and carvings in caves which have been attributed to the Cro-Magnon Era, however, certain signs can be interpreted as the burning of incense and use of sweet-smelling products of herbal substances.

Some esoteric researchers hold a theory that the Cro-Magnons may have been descendants of the survivors of Atlantis, which would account for the sudden increase in the aesthetic practices of the people. A factor that favors the belief is that, according to the earliest historical evidence, the inhabitants of the territory surrounding the

13

Mediterranean—the Carthaginians, the people in Northern Africa, Egyptians, Arabians, Israelites, Phoenicians, Greeks, and Romans—were the earliest-recorded users of herbal products as incense, perfumes, and medicines.

It is logical to assume that from the use of incense and perfume and the application of herbal products to curative purposes and the healing arts, it is but a short step to their utilization as food and in the embellishment of foods, to make them more palatable. Although no tangible proof is available, it is not only possible but even probable that herbal products were instinctively used as food, even before the beginnings of so-called civilization.

In every phase of human existence, from the earliest times to the intricacy of modern life, we find that herbs and herbal products have been and are vital in the economy of living.

Herbs and herbal products are not uniformly identical. In the plant world Nature provides an intricately organized and systematically controlled alchemical and chemical laboratory.

Chlorophyll, the green coloring matter of plants, may be called the "Chief Engineer" in the alchemical process of PHOTOSYNTHESIS, which means the chemical combination of the oxygen in the air, under the motivation of the energy of light, with the water from the soil to form starch and cellulose, the basic ingredients of all plant and animal tissues.

Each species or variety of plant has its own special "liking" for the particular chemical elements or compounds

14

that it stores within its cells along with the starch and cellulose. The term *herbal products* may be said to refer to those individually stored compounds, whether or not the plant has developed woody tissue as part of its general metabolism. The broad study of HERBALISM, then, will include an investigation of plant products in relation to the economy of living and to the benefit of human welfare.

It is probable that in addition to the use of plants as food, in every country on earth when the people had developed to the awareness of worship of some deity, herbs and plant products were burned as incense or offered in sacrifice to the heathen gods. Of all nations, however, Ancient Egypt was undoubtedly the first to expand that practice to include many of the related functions of which we have familiar examples today.

The early science and art of perfumery and perfume manufacturing began in Ancient Egypt. It is questionable whether the Egyptians were the first to use herbal products as medicines in alleviating pain or curing diseases, because that is so closely related to the early priestly activities—votary offerings to please or appease the Gods.

Earliest Chinese records describe the use of incense and odorous materials among Oriental people. It was ritualistic, relating to religious ceremonies, weddings, and funerals.

However, the hieroglyphic records from the early Egyptian culture have provided the only continuous account of the evolution of what may be called the "odor industry" and its continuous growth to its present multi-billion dollar, universal status.

15

The country of the Pharaohs has furnished not only its hieroglyphic record which has increased interest among historians, but also material evidence to corroborate the written or pictured descriptions. When the tomb of Pharaoh Tutankhamen was discovered and opened late in the year 1922, among the treasures in the burial chamber were vessels that indubitably were designed to hold incense and perfumes. Of course during the period of more than three thousand years since his mummy had been placed there, the perfumes had evaporated, but the odor remained in the receptacles as indisputable proof of the materials they once had contained.

It has been determined from records and factual evidence that the "heavenly odors" of perfumes were somehow linked with the hope of immortality, and perhaps that is why perfumes and other herbal products were always buried with the mummy. Herbal products were also used in the mummification process.

Can honey be considered an herbal product? The answer, of course, is "Yes." Honey originates in the pollen and nectar of plants and flowers—in the chemical laboratory of Nature's vast storehouse. The bees are the engineers and operators who take the raw materials, the nectar, pollen, and juices of the plants and in the marvelous alchemical laboratories of their bodies predigest these substances to form the perfect product which has so many uses, even beyond its value as food.

A legend as fabulous as a fairy tale tells of the ancient

16

cave man who was returning from the hunt late in the afternoon of a warm day in summer. He came to an open glade in the forest. The ground around him was covered with beautiful flowers of many colors.

Unlike many of his fellow inhabitants of the caves, this man, whose name may have been "Oooomah," was beginning to differentiate between the "danger odors" and the "delightful smells." So he stopped to rest for a few minutes to enjoy the pleasant aroma and to notice the many-hued carpet of blossoms.

An insect lit on his arm. He felt a sharp pain. Then the insect flew, to join a swarm of others on the trunk of a nearby tree. Oooomah was curious. He investigated. There was some kind of nest there, and a sticky material was oozing from the cakelike object. He reached up to feel it and another bee sting was his reward. Angered, he put the finger into his mouth to ease the pain, and his facial expression changed, as if the god of pleasure were smiling on him. That sticky stuff tasted wonderful! At the risk of more insect stings, he reached for more and tore the cake from its fastenings on the tree. This was something he must share with his mate and neighbors in the caves. Leaving the product of his hunting—the carcass of a young creodont in the flower-bedecked meadow, he hurried through the forest to the home caves, carrying the precious honeycomb.

He greeted his mate and children with gestures and signs and grins. What a wonderful discovery he had made!

17

Their grunts of satisfaction and exclamations of joy told him that they agreed the sweet-tasting sticky stuff was delightful.

Attracted by their cries of happiness, the denizens of neighboring caves flocked around, to see what all the excitement was about. Oooomah explained, with many guttural words and much waving of hands and arms. Then there was enough honey left so that each one could have a taste.

A general stampede followed. They all went into the forest to find some of that delightful sticky stuff for themselves. A happy epoch in food and nutrition had been inaugurated. Since that time, in legend and history, honey has proved itself to be one of the most useful and beneficial products of Nature's Alchemy.

In the Old Testament, in the Bible, the "Promised Land" —the goal of the Israelites after their captivity in Egypt— the Land of Canaan, is referred to as "a land flowing with milk and honey." Milk is often called a perfect food, and we find that honey is not only a wonderful food, but throughout history and in the folklore of many nations, it is valued for its healing properties, its medicinal qualities as well.

The human mind is a vast storehouse. "Everything is becoming." When one or more of our human senses is affected by a change in Nature, we have a SENSATION. A sensation repeated many times furnishes recognition, or PERCEPTION. Memory's contemplation views these percepts in the light of past experiences and we have APPER-

CEPTIONS, and it is these apperceptions which furnish the raw materials of which IMAGINATION is built. The combined apperceptions of the people in a tribe or community give rise to legends or folk tales that in their origins are based on factual experiences. One observed fact is added to another, the benefits of their application become fully appreciated, a tribal custom is born, and the evolution of folklore is on the way.

In every nation and every land, these primeval customs and so-called superstitions have merged into the historical records that provide the data for the study of anthropology. In the light of modern scientific knowledge and research, many facts have been verified, which were formerly thought to be "old wives' tales," or pure superstition.

Facts gleaned from the study of the folk legends of the various nations show a close agreement in many particulars in connection with the use of herbs and herbal products. This is especially true with regard to honey. The legendary discovery of honey and its use as food is reputedly mentioned in some of the earliest historical records.

In recent years our so-called civilization has largely replaced honey as a table sweet, but the indisputable fact remains that this natural product of Nature's Alchemy is the only food that offers many health-giving qualities, both physiological and nutritional, as well as its satisfying sweetness.

It is an accepted conclusion that honey was used by the ancient Egyptians as a curative agent in addition to its function in food and nutrition. In the folklore of various

19

nations references have been found to verify this characteristic of Nature's Alchemical product. In the United States in recent years, the research departments of several Universities have conducted experiments to show that disease germs cannot live in the presence of honey, which is an abundant source of the element, potassium. Biochemists have determined that the potassium in honey withdraws the moisture that is essential to the existence of bacterial growth.

Bulletin No. 252, published by the Colorado Agricultural College, gives an interesting report of the results of one of these early experiments. Many disease-producing germs were placed, each, in a culture of pure honey. The bacillus of typhoid fever died in less than 48 hours. The germ of paratyphoid, which is found in bowel movements and water, died in five hours. The bacteria that are responsible for the disease bronchopneumonia and chronic bronchitis died after three days. Many other specific types of microorganisms, each producing diseased conditions in the human body, are listed, with the same result. Within a few hours or a few days, the bacteria died. These results have been duplicated and verified in other Universities, and by the Bureau of Entomology in Washington, D.C. This proof cannot be disputed. Disease-producing microorganisms cannot live in the presence of honey.

Biochemical research shows that for perfect human metabolism certain chemical elements are required. These elements must be present in the food we eat, in a form available for assimilation.

20

Chemical analysis shows that honey contains mineral elements that often are short in food. Aluminum, calcium, chlorine, copper, iron, manganese, magnesium, phosphorus, potassium, silicon, and sodium, all or any of which may be lacking in the "processed" food the average family buys in today's markets, are all present in honey. Amounts of each element may vary, because some soils may be deficient in certain elements that plants need, but they are all in honey in the infinitesimal quantity necessary for human metabolism.

Legend and folklore associate another product with honey. While apple-cider vinegar is not strictly an herbal product, its beneficial effects are so closely connected with, and complementary to those of honey in ameliorating many ailments that may be caused by diet deficiencies that it is worth noting. It has been related by some that a mixture of honey and apple-cider vinegar in a glass of water has furnished the mineral elements, particularly potassium, to provide a healthy condition in the body and also to promote restful sleep.

The germicidal property of honey has been proved. The folklore of the people of many nationalities, from rural New England, Canada, the Middle West, the descendants of the early French and Spanish settlers of New Orleans, Louisiana, Mississippi, Alabama, California, the North Pacific states have mentioned the beneficial qualities of honey and the mixture with apple-cider vinegar in relieving the unpleasantness of many common ailments, particularly respiratory congestions.

21

Several reports have been received regarding the use of honey as applied to skin infections. According to the statements, the results were amazing. Within two days, the infection disappeared and in less than a week healing was complete.

Honey was recognized for its medicinal value in addition to its use as food, even in Ancient Egypt and the Mediterranean countries. Through the ages since that time, many people have used and are using honey for its curative power.

CHAPTER TWO

Aromas for the Gods

WITH THE POSSIBLE EXCEPTION OF THE AMERI-
can Indians, people of the various nations, in their progress
toward full awareness of their environment, attributed
anthropomorphic characteristics to the deities they worshipped. That is, they considered their gods as superhu-
mans in exalted form, with greater powers, advanced
accomplishments, and increased capacities for exercise of
their emotions. That these manifestations often were anything but godlike is evidenced by many legends in Classi-
cal Mythology. Gods of Ancient Greece and Rome and
other Mediterranean countries often exhibited human
frailties in aggravated form. Their jealousy, anger, vindic-
tiveness, and covetousness had to be propitiated in some
manner, or woe betide their human subjects!

Since these gods possessed the emotions and sense per-
ceptions of people, what would please men and women
probably would give satisfaction to the gods. People enjoy
the fragrance of flowers and aromatic herbs. Therefore,
sweet odors of burning plants would delight the gods. If
they were angry, it would appease their ire; if they were in

joyful mood, they would appreciate that their human subjects were thoughtful of their pleasure.

Only a few of the more enlightened individuals may have reasoned that they, themselves, might benefit by this act of homage. From that beginning the esoteric significance of incense has developed through the ages.

The Bible is full of references in the Old Testament, about the use of incense by the ancient Hebrews. While they did not worship a multiplicity of gods, as did the neighboring countries surrounding them, all evidence seems to indicate that their conception of Jehovah was anthropomorphic; that His wrath could be appeased by sacrifices and burnt offerings, and by the lavish use of sweet-smelling incense.

Many anthropologists believe that the human race evolved through graduated stages or eras. First came the hunting stage, when the food was predominantly flesh food, from animals, the products of the chase. In those very early times, each individual was a law unto himself, or, since the mating instinct is a fundamental law of Nature, the family became the unit of existence. It probably was during this era of developing knowledge that certain herbs were discovered to be palatable adjuncts to the daily food ration. Then, with the discovery of fire, both herbs and meat began to be prepared in a more elaborate way. The ingrained feeling of dependence on some higher power than himself gave rise to the idea of votive offerings to these deities.

The gregarious instinct, the natural desire for companionship led families to group together, and the clan or tribe appeared. The individual offerings to the gods gradually became systematized into an organized, definite form or custom. It is significant that the folklore and legendary stories that have come down to the present from all nations follow the same general pattern; that the offerings to the gods were flesh, fowl, and plant—a food sacrifice, which would please the gods because food was valuable and sometimes hard to obtain.

Among the many herbs and herbal products mentioned in the earlier and later legends and literature of the Mediterranean lands, as ingredients of incense, perfumes, and beautifying oils, were aloes, myrrh, spikenard, and frankincense. These were all indigenous to the lands surrounding the Mediterranean. They were highly prized, sometimes rare, and very costly. Spikenard, very aromatic, used in incense and perfumes, comes from a shrub, native to Northern India and Tibet, in the Himalayas. Its botanical name is *Nardostachys jatamansi,* an herb of the Valerian family. Myrrh is an aromatic gum resin, obtained from a tree, *Cummiphora abyssinica,* a native of Africa and Arabia. It is a mixture of resin, gum, and the essential oil, myrrhol. This gum resin has a bitter, pungent taste, but when used in incense and perfume, it imparts a heavenly odor, and is highly valued.

Aloe, or aloes, is the name applied to any member of the Genus *Aloe,* an Old World shrub belonging to the Lily family. It is a true herb, and is the source of various drugs and incense materials and perfume products. The American Aloe is the century plant. Frankincense is a gum resin from various trees found in East Africa. It is very aromatic and is used in incense and in medicine. It is also an ingredient of certain perfumes, particularly of the oriental type.

In the development of incense and perfumes from herbal products, the Oriental people, Chinese, Japanese, and the inhabitants of the Malay states probably reached what to them was a degree of perfection even earlier than the inhabitants of the Mediterranean countries. It is questionable, however, if any country preceded Egypt in that respect. While the East Indian and Japanese incense is much superior to that from most other sources, there is a wide difference between it and the typically Chinese incense and perfumes. The early Chinese reputedly discovered and used *musk*, both in incense and perfumes, and while musk is a valuable adjunct to the perfumer's art, it is an animal product, and not herbal in its origin. But the Chinese odors both in incense and perfumes seem to be stronger or even obnoxious, compared to the other Oriental types.

It is significant that the science of odors as related to personal adornment and religious practices, as well as the deeper esoteric development, apparently had its origin in Egypt and in the neighboring countries on the south shore of the Mediterranean and in Asia Minor and Phoenicia. From that source the custom spread through the Balkans, Greece, Rome, and all of Southern Europe.

The earliest historical records indicate that the culture of Ancient Egypt was extremely high and exceeded by many years those of several of the inhabited neighboring lands. That fact poses a natural question: Does it have a bearing on the theory that the survivors of the Atlantean disaster settled in the Valley of the Nile and brought their reputed culture with them? If there is a connection, it would explain many things.

There is a widely accepted theory that the geography of a country would act as a strong determinant in the historical development of that nation. Natural land barriers, and even water barriers, will tend to limit emigration or immigration, to a certain extent, at least. In the study of history, it is evident that great changes in the autonomy of a nation came about only after invasion or conquest nullified these natural barriers. That may explain why the use of incense and perfume by the central Europeans seems to have developed later than in the Mediterranean countries.

The ancient city of Carthage, on the north coast of Africa, near the site of the present Tunis, was reputedly founded by the semilegendary Queen Dido, but in all probability was an outgrowth of small trading posts that were established by Phoenicians about 900 B.C. Probably the beginnings were small, but since the culture of the ancient Phoenicians was well developed, even these small beginnings felt the influence of the Phoenician worship of many gods. Like the Phoenicians, the inhabitants of Carthage practiced fire worship, with votary offerings to their principal gods, chief among whom was Moloch, or Baal-Ammon, symbolical of the destructive power of the sun. In

27

addition to the burning of strong incense, there was reputed to be a fiery furnace in the Temples of Moloch,
where human sacrifices were offered on occasion to appease the terrible wrath of this bloodthirsty god. Of the
more beneficent deities, the Moon Goddess, Ashtoreth, pat-
terned after the Greek Astarte, later became known in
Carthage as Tanith. She required the offerings of sweet-
smelling incense and perfumes only. Another important
member of the Carthaginian hierarchy was Melkart, who
appears to resemble the Hercules of the Greeks. Great
honor was attributed to him, and especial gifts were trans-
mitted to his temples, even as far as Tyre, in Phoenicia. The
Carthaginian God of the sea, whose name has become lost
in recorded story, was undoubtedly similar to the Greek
Poseidon, and the fish-god Dagon of the Philistines. All of
these gods could be worshipped and placated by votary
offerings of incense. However, none of them except Moloch
required human sacrifices.

The Carthaginians were not a literary people, from all
available records. Their strength lay in merchandising,
trading, and in their maritime prowess, in which they excelled.

The entire history of this fabled nation, Carthage, the
City-State, was one of belligerent warfare and conquest.
The more lands they could conquer, the more trade they
would have. Their chief opponents were Greece and Rome,
and their colonization extended as far west as the west coast
of Africa and Spain and to the north into Gaul. It is significant that during periods of conquest, many of the customs

and religious practices of the conquerors seem to be absorbed and adopted by the conquered.

In the very early days, when Egypt was expanding her power to become the leaders of the known world, that influence is reflected in the votive offerings to the gods in Phoenicia. Then came Carthage and Greece, and finally Rome. A similarity in the practices of the use of herbal products, both as sacrifices to their gods and in other ways as well, apparently is progressively evident.

Throughout the series of conquests and defeats known to history as the Punic Wars, the struggle for supremacy continued. The Latin name for Phoenicians was *POENI*, hence the name, Punic. From 264 B.C. until the utter defeat of the Carthaginians by Publius Cornelius Scipio Æmilianus in 146 B.C., the turbulent City-State continued to wield her influence in lands surrounding the Mediterranean area. What was left of Carthage became a Roman province, and its use of herbal products became identified with the Roman practices. Attempts to restore the City were unsuccessful until 29 B.C., when the Emperor Augustus Caesar, Julius Caesar's successor, rebuilt it and it became one of the most prominent cities of the Roman Empire. From that time, until its complete destruction by the Arabs in A.D. 698, use of herbal products for personal adornment and food embellishment took precedence over the votary offerings to the gods.

Mention has been made that the discovery and development of the use of musk in incense and perfumes has been attributed to the Chinese. Although musk is not primarily a

29

vegetable product and cannot be classified with herbs, its use through the ages has been so closely associated with the herbal products that mention of it is not out of harmony with the scope of this work.

However, there is one outstanding example of a true herb that characterizes the Chinese picture, dating back more than two thousand years, even before the days of Confucius. Botanically, this herb belongs to the family *Araliaceae*, which has similar characteristics to the family *Umbelliferae*, except that the fruit is a one-seeded drupe—similar to a cherry—a soft, fleshy fruit surrounding a hard-shelled stone, or seed. This family of plants contains over fifty genera, the principal ones of which are *Aralia*, represented by many species, including the Spikenard and Sarsaparillas; *Hedera*, of which the Ivy is an example; *Echinopanax*, the "devil's club"; and *Panax*, the ginseng.

The genus *Panax* includes two specific herbs which are almost fabulous in their claimed characteristics, and properties and uses. The plant which is native to China is *Panax schinseng*, a true herb, often growing to a height of perhaps two or three feet. It has very small green flowers, berries of a deep scarlet color, and compound leaves consisting of five leaflets, something like the five-leafed ivy. It is the roots, however, that are of greatest interest.

The American species, *Panax quinquefolia*, differs very little from the Asiatic variety, and the roots of both are identical in their preparation and use. Certain writings attributed to Confucius praised the roots of this herb for their curative powers. Since Confucius lived more than 500

30

years before the Christian Era, its use by the Chinese antedated that time by probably hundreds of years. It is still used in Chinese medicine.

The ancient way of preparing the root for use was by a secret process, known only to Chinese apothecaries. A perfect root, not marred or broken, was cured to a clear translucency by this secret process. Today, such a root may bring several hundred dollars per ounce in the Chinese market, many times the international price of gold.

Prepared in this fashion, encased in fine silk and placed in a small jeweled casket, a root was considered an appropriate gift for a powerful Chinese potentate. Through the ages, ginseng has been considered the herbal "fountain of youth" and particularly beneficial as an aphrodisiac to restore vitality and vigor to the aged. The Chinese believe that it will prolong life. Many wonderful cures have been attributed to this root by the Oriental people.

Back in the eighteenth century, some enterprising Yankee, probably a sea captain, in the Oriental trade, got an idea. He knew that a similar species of plant grew in his native New England, and he carried several hundred pounds of the roots with him on his next trip. The response was tremendous, and the Yankee's fortune was made. He returned a rich man. Today, there are millions of people in Southeast Asia who are eager to buy even more than we can produce. The boom is continuing, and the price is still spiraling upward. Pharmacologists have as yet failed to discover any useful properties in the root, and it is not listed in the United States Pharmacopeia.

31

It requires five to eight years of growth to produce a root of salable size. However, with the price as high as it is, and still climbing, some farmers in the United States have included ginseng quite extensively in their crop schedule.

To some people, the taste of the ginseng root may seem to be somewhat unpleasant. It has a faint bitter-sweet tang that is reminiscent of the aftertaste of licorice.

The Chinese believe that a tea made from ginseng root will cure tuberculosis, and will cure or prevent many other diseases, including fatigue of both body and mind. It cannot be classified as a "fad" because of its long history as a staple article of merchandise and its steadily increasing demand.

No records have been found that show the use of powdered ginseng root in mixtures of herbs used as incense. It would be an interesting experiment to add ginseng root, powdered, or the dried leaves or fruit to other herbal substances and to burn the mixture as incense to discover what effect, if any, would be evident.

CHAPTER THREE

Mysterious Stonehenge

IT IS PERHAPS NATURAL THAT A SIMILARITY IN customs, beliefs, and practices, particularly in the worship of certain deities, will lead to the conclusion that there has been a close connection or relationship between two or more widely separated human societies. Such a comparison exists between the Druids and some other even more ancient people. Early researchers reported the resemblance of Druidism to the religion of the Phoenicians, the Chaldeans of Assyria, and even the Brachmans of Hindustan. The religions of each of these nations were permeated with sublime precepts, consoling promises, and reverential awe. One authority even goes so far as to state that the religious practices of all of these no doubt came from the same origin, the religion of Noah before the flood!

From all available information, the Druids worshipped one Supreme Being and other lesser gods. They erected altars of earth or unhewn stone, where their adoration was characterized by ritual, herbal offerings, and other sacrifices. They were particularly devoted to the mistletoe, especially when it grew on oak trees.

While the mistletoe is a parasitic plant, it nevertheless is a true herb. The European variety, *Viscum album,* is an evergreen, with yellowish-green leaves and rather small, inconspicuous flowers, which develop into glutinous white berries. There is an American variety, *Phoradendron flavescens,* which is practically identical. The Druids attributed great healing power to the mistletoe, especially when it grew on the oak trees. They called it the "All Heal" plant and it was featured in their religious practices and rituals, which were held in oak groves, where the mistletoe grew profusely.

Tradition, legends, folklore, and fairy tales all have beginnings. It is reasonable to suppose that the early stages of these phenomena may be called truths that promenade in fancy clothing. Behind every folk custom is some fact or necessity, real or fancied. It is interesting to note that many procedures that we recognize as folk habits were developed in connection with the use of herbs or herbal products.

Many of the practices of the inhabitants of early Britain, the Celts and Druids, for example, evidently were a development from a combination of three sources. The first influence apparently was an almost fanatical adherence to the tenets of their religion. What might be considered their political economy was next in importance. The third factor that affected their individual and communal habits was the increasing commercial contacts, particularly with the Carthaginian colonists and the Phoenicians.

According to all available evidence, the Supreme Being

34

worshipped by the Druids combined both male and female aspects, and was revealed always to humans in three different manifestations, which might be considered prophetic of the belief in the Trinity by the Christian churches of today. This chief god apparently was not confined to one place, but was universal in all Nature and could be contacted by using the products of Nature in their worship. Their principal mystical appeal was in connection with the *mistletoe,* but they used other herbs as well, particularly in their healing arts. Their ritualistic worship of this omnipotent deity was revealed through their reverence for the mistletoe.

Druidism was not only the religion of the people. It was the controlling power in the government of the state. The ruler, with absolute authority, was the Arch Druid. There were three lesser groups in the priesthood, under him, and answerable to him. The highest were the much-revered and intellectual philosophers, who controlled and managed the organization and operation of the state and the activities of the priesthood. They also presided over and exercised their power in the fundamental, deeply ritualistic mysteries of the oak groves where the ceremonies were held, and which were linked with the mistletoe and other herbs and herbal products. The oak tree was sacred to them, and the name given to these "Keepers of the Oak groves" was "Derwydd," from the ancient Celtic language, "Derw" meaning "Oak" and "ydd," meaning "to be identified with" or "to be a part of." It was pronounced like "Droo-idd."

The next in authority, under the Arch Druid, were the

35

Bards. They were the musicians, who recited and sang praises to the Supreme God, and sang chants during the sacred ceremonies in the Groves. They also were required to register all genealogies and keep records of historical events. They were called "The Unspoiled Ones" or "The Pure Ones" and were greatly honored by the people.

The third class of the governing priesthood were the beginners, or neophytes, who were directly responsible to the Druids and of course under the control of the Arch Druid. Their particular duties were of an investigative character; that is, they delved into the exact properties of all Nature and offered the sacrifices on the altar during the ceremonies.

Because this combination of religion and state was absolute and continued in effect, with possible minor variations, for several hundred years, it is safe to assume that this dictatorship was a benign one. The Arch Druid did not succeed to office through political chicanery, but earned the exalted rank by a long course of exacting study. This included a thorough knowledge of the sacred tenets of Druidism, and proficiency in the sciences of astronomy, navigation, and medicine, as well as a working knowledge of mechanical operations. Proficiency in foreign languages was also stressed.

The Druid state was renowned for its educational culture in the Mediterranean countries as well as in Gaul as early as the sixth century B.C. One of the Derwydd, of the Philosopher Class, is said to have visited in Greece, and to have become a warm friend of Pythagoras, who found him of similar mind and outlook on life. In fact, many comments were made at the fluency which marked the use of the Greek language by this man from beyond the great sea.

The principles of Druidism were said to be all in verse. It has been estimated that there were more than twenty thousand stanzas. They were all in triplet form, since apparently the sacred number of the Druidic philosophy was three. To learn all of those by heart, from the spoken word, would require many years of deep study.

In their study of medicines and the healing arts, they went back to Nature's Alchemy and the health-giving and healing qualities of growing plants, herbs, and herbal products. Their most potent remedies included the mistletoe in some form. No wonder they called it the "All Heal" plant.

Some of the herbs used by the Druids, particularly in their healing arts, included, besides the mistletoe, the common Vervain which is a true herb and a member of the Verbena family, *Verbenaceae* and its principal genus, *Verbena*. Of this genus there are more than 100 species, natively distributed over Europe and tropical America. The main European species used by the Druids was *Verbena officinalis*, which grew to a height of about twelve inches. It bore delicate, small white flowers, which were very fragrant. As was the case with most of the herbs used by the Druids, there was a ritual connected with gathering this plant. It was to be picked only under certain conditions of Nature: When the Dog Star was rising; at night when the sun did not shine; during the dark of the moon, the vervain must be dug up by the roots with an iron implement. It must be held in the left hand and waved aloft in the air, with the proper incantations. The flowers, leaves, stalks, and roots must be dried separately in the shade. When dry, they must be infused in a special kind of wine. The principal use of this concoction was to cure the bites of poisonous insects or serpents.

The white vervain, *Verbena urticaefolia,* found in tropical America, is a perennial herb about seven inches in height. It bears scented white flowers.

Another species, which blooms with purplish or blue flowers, and grows to a height of about fifteen inches, is native to Chile and Brazil. Its botanical name is *Verbena erinoides,* and its common name is Moss Verbena.

Verbena canadensis is native to Southern Mexico. It often reaches a height of sixteen to eighteen inches and its flowers may be white or rose-colored or possibly lilac-tinted. It is sometimes called the Clump Verbena.

Many of the verbena plants that are common in our gardens, particularly in "old-fashioned" gardens, are hybrid varieties, cultivated artificially. Whether or not they would show the mystical qualities attributed to the ancient Druid usage in incense or infusions would be an interesting field for experimentation.

The red-flowered herb, *Verbena chamaedryfolia,* is native to several locations in central South America. Both *Verbena phlogiflora,* which bears rose-colored flowers, and *Verbena incisa,* whose flowers are purple, grow profusely in the southern part of South America. The flowers of *Ver-*

bena teucrioides are usually white or tinged with lemon yellow or pink. It also is native to South America.

The common garden hybrid probably most familiar of all is *Verbena hortensis* and its flowers may be varied, sometimes of one color, often striped or with an "eye" in the center. It blooms through the summer until late in the fall.

With all the vervains, there must be some quality, either aroma, taste, or other effect which attracts insect pests. The natural question arises: Was it that quality that motivated the mystical ritual of gathering the plants and their use for insect stings by the ancient Druids?

The plant known by the common name "Selago" really belongs to the family of club mosses, the *Selaginaceae*. The genus, *Selaginella,* contains over seven hundred species of what may be called "Fern allies," and grows in many parts of the world.

To the ancient Druids, it was a charm as well as a medicine, and like other herbal products, its gathering was strictly according to the prescribed ritual. A member of the Ovades, or Neophyte Priests, must dress all in white, then bathe his feet in running water and offer sacrifices of bread and wine. Then he was required to wrap the skirt of his white robe around his right hand, and using a hook made of brass he would dig up the entire plant by the roots and immediately cover it with a white cloth. It was used as a charm to ward off evil spirits, and in medicine, combined with certain herbs of the mint family and with the mistletoe, it would cure various diseases.

The SAMOLUS—(*Samolus floribundus*) grew in damp places and is known today by the common name, Water Pimpernel, or Brookweed. Its white flowers are in bloom from June to August. The Priests who gathered this herb must conform to a rigid ritual. First they must go without food for several days. While fasting, they must approach the plant and without looking behind them, they must dig it up by the roots with the left hand. Then the plants were laid in a trough where cattle drank. After it was thoroughly bruised, it was supposed to be a cure for several kinds of ailments, distempers, and weaknesses.

The herb whose common names are CARPENTER WEED or SELF-HEAL or HEAL-ALL, and whose Botanical name is *Prunella vulgaris*, was highly prized by the Druids. Its flowers are either purple or white, and grow in a spikelike cluster toward the end of the stem. It belongs to the Mint family, *Lamiaceae*. The ritual accompanying its gathering was similar to that used with the vervains. Its dried flowers were mixed with other herbs and burned as incense, and it found many uses in medicinal mixtures, as well.

Clinopodium vulgaris, the common name of which is BASIL, was often in use. It is also a member of the LAMIACEAE, or Mint family. It was a perennial herb that grew in thickets or waste places, and attained a height of from four to sixteen inches. Its flowers were either white or purple, and both flowers and leaves were used as an offering to their chief god and the lesser hero-gods. This herb has a rootstock, which also was used in their worship and probably all of the plant was used as a food adjunct as well.

Another Mint that these herb-loving people used in their worship was the WATER HOREHOUND—*Lycopus communis*, which was almost odorless, but which was used in their vegetable offerings to their gods. It also had a rootstock. Moisture loving, it grew in wet places in the woods. Its small flowers were shaped like an opened bell.

A plant which grew in moist flat places, also a member of the Mint family, seems, in description, to resemble *Trichostema oblongum*, whose common name is BLUE CURLS. It grew to a height of from four to twelve inches. The small flowers were clustered in the axils of the leaves, where they joined the stem. Ordinarily of a sky-blue color, occasionally they were purple or pink, and bell-shaped. According to legend, the plant, which bloomed in June and July, often was woven into garlands used in certain ritualistic rites.

A plant which was similar to the common FIGWORT, *Scrofularia occidentalis*, grew on low ground in thickets and woods. It had small, greenish-colored flowers, with numerous seeds, and was used in their healing preparations.

Another herb of the Figwort family that seems to resemble *Pentstemmon virens*, with deep blue flowers, was in use by the Druids.

Another herb belonging to the Mint family, growing to a height of twelve to sixteen inches, was the common SPEARMINT or PEPPERMINT, *Mentha spicata*. As with ours today, the leaves were very fragrant, with the clean, refreshing odor of peppermint. The flowers also were pleas-

41

ing, with their whorls forming a spike at the end of the stem. These spikes of flowers were usually of a rose-pink color. The herb had a rootstock, and the entire plant was dried in the shade, and used both in incense and medicines, and possibly as an embellishment in food preparation as well. It grew in open fields and waste places.

Although in legend and history emphasis has been placed on all the religious and mystical aspects of the Druid society, it must not be thought that all members were of the priestly orders. In what may be called the "Governing Class" the Arch Druid was the absolute ruler. Under him were the Derwydd, or Philosophers, then the Bards—musicians, singers, and advocates of the Arts—and the Ovades, or priests, who were the actual "operators" of the ritualistic acts. Ordinarily they dressed in white but their robes were green when they were performing their sacerdotal duties at the altars in the groves.

Those in the Druidistic society who were not members of one of the priestly groups were the workers who received the benefits of the philosophy and learning. There was little or no poverty. One of the fundamentals of Druidism was to help the unfortunates and to furnish training in the work that may be assigned to them by the Arch Druid and the Derwydd. The Bards and the Ovades figured largely in the application of this training.

Among the lay members were engineers, construction workers, merchants, those who assisted the philosophers (Derwydd), the ones who were associated with the Astronomers, and others who might be classified as laborers

42

in various categories. But all were versed in the benefits and mysteries of the various herbs and herbal products which were used not only in their religious rituals, but in their daily life as well.

One practice of the ancient Britons, including the Celts and Druids, was the tattooing of their bodies with mystical designs, by cutting the skin and rubbing into the lines so cut a strong infusion of Woad. This was an herb belonging to the Mustard family (*Brassicaceae*). This herb was native to Europe and grew in waste places to a height of from four to twelve inches. Its botanical name is *Isatis tinctoria*. The blue-green leaves were lance-shaped, sometimes slightly toothed. The yellow flowers were in the form of a raceme, at the end of the stems. The leaves of this herb, when soaked or steeped in water, furnish an intense blue dye. Imported from Europe, this herb can now be found in desert places in the United States, particularly in Utah.

In every phase of human existence, from the earliest days of legend and folklore to the present enlightenment and experimentation, the contribution of herbs and herbal products furnishes a fascinating study of Nature's Alchemy.

CHAPTER FOUR

God's Gift to Man

A STUDY OF HISTORICAL GEOLOGY REVEALS THE fact that the earliest living things on the earth, both in the sea and on land, were plants—first, the simplest forms of one-celled organisms. Then, with the increasing complexity of physiological division of labor, the various species of multicelled plants developed as environments provided changing patterns for existence.

Available evidences seem to indicate that the early Hebrews lived on the fruits of the field and the herbs of the earth. They were vegetarians. That is, their use of animals in their worship was for sacrificial purposes only.

In both the Old and the New Testament in the Bible, there are many references to the use of herbs, in incense and ritual and also as food. Some of these applications are definitely traceable to Egyptian influence, while others are more like the Phoenician or Carthaginian customs.

Herbs, as used for food, may be classified as Green Herbs and Potherbs. In the first category, we consider all the herbs and herbal products that are eaten raw or used raw in salads or as garnishes. Certain oils that are herbal products also may be mentioned under the heading of Green Herbs.

Potherbs are those that are cooked, usually boiled, or used to flavor boiled foods. The fact that they are classified as potherbs does not mean they are never eaten raw. On the contrary, many of them are even more palatable raw than cooked.

No references have been found that would indicate that the early inhabitants of Palestine, before the time of Noah and the Biblical flood ever used animal food. In the King James Version of the Bible, in Genesis 1:11 and 12, "And God said, Let the earth bring forth grass, the herb yielding seed, *and* the fruit tree yielding fruit after his kind, whose seed is in itself, upon the earth: and it was so. And the earth brought forth grass, *and* herb yielding seed after his kind, and the tree yielding fruit, whose seed *was* in itself, after his kind: and God saw that *it was* good."

Animals were used in their worship as sacrifices and burnt offerings, but there is no mention of the eating of flesh up to the time of the repopulation of the earth after the waters of the traditional deluge receded. There is ample evidence, however, that herbs and herbal products formed a major portion of the food of the ancient Hebrews both before and after Noah's time.

There are at least twenty Biblical citations that relate specific instances of the use of green herbs as food, by name. Some of these are repeated many times. Undoubtedly the Hebrew housewife concocted many different and new mixtures of herbs to please the tastes of her family.

46

We find in the Book of Second Kings, in Chapter 4:39, a notation about green herbs and potherbs as well:

"One went out into the field to gather herbs, and found a wild vine, and gathered thereof wild gourds his lap full, and came and shred *them* into the pot of pottage: for they knew *them* not." In the same Chapter barley meal and corn are mentioned.

In almost every book in the Bible there is mention of both green herbs and potherbs as food for the people. In the Second Book of Samuel, Chapter Seventeen, Verses 28 and 29, we read, ". . . wheat, and barley, and flour, and parched *corn,* and beans, and lentiles, and parched *pulse,* and honey, . . . for David, and for the people that *were* with him, to eat: for they said, The people *is* hungry and weary and thirsty, in the wilderness."

Wild Thyme (*Thymus serpyllum*) was used both as a green herb and a potherb for flavoring, in cookery, its mintlike quality adding zest to the mixture of foods to which it was added. Other members of the Mint family were among the "appetizers" in the preparation of foods.

Pepper, mustard, garlic, several varieties of paprika or red pepper, parsley (*Petroselinum latifolium*), tarragon (*Artemisia dracunculus*) which is a member of the Thistle family—and many other aromatic herbs garnished the food of the ancient Hebrews, even as these and other condiments are used today to add flavor.

After the Exodus of the Israelites from Egypt, we find radishes mentioned in connection with their food. Radishes were known in Egypt from the earliest days, so it is safe to

47

assume that their use by the Hebrew people began during the so-called captivity.

Artichokes, as we know them today, undoubtedly were developed by the Ancient Romans from the original member of the Thistle family of herbs. The genus *Helianthus,* of the Family CARDUACEAE, includes the Sunflower, and what is known as the Ground Artichoke. The delicate "hearts" were among the green herbs in Palestine and also were mixed with others in their "pottage."

The leaves of many herbs were eaten as "Greens," either raw in salads with salt and other spices or boiled in their pottage. Among others, the Israelites knew *Leontodon erythospermun,* or *Leontodon taraxacom,* both of which are varieties of the common Dandelion, and both of which were imported into the United States from Europe and the Near East. This herb belongs to the Chicory family, and its leaves were used either as greens or as potherbs mixed and boiled with other green leaves.

Capers were used as condiments. The capers were flower buds of a low shrub or herb belonging to the family Caparidaceae, native to the Mediterranean countries. The buds were used as flavoring in other food mixtures.

Basil, belonging to the Lamiaceae, or Mint family, has the specific name, *Clinopodium vulgare.* It was used in many ways, as flavoring, and mixed in with the green herbs. The Basil which we use today comes from plants that were originally imported from Eurasia.

Tansy, *Tanacetum vulgare,* is an herb belonging to the Thistle Family, *Carduaceae.* It has yellow flowers, is very aromatic, with a slightly bitter taste, and it was used by the Israelites in food mixtures or as tea, for its medicinal properties, and as a tonic. The tansy which we have today was originally imported from Eurasia, where it is a native herb.

Several varieties of beans were staple foods, with celery, broccoli, garlic, and onions functioning both as green herbs and potherbs. Lettuce also was grown and used.

One herb which is mentioned was known as the "Colocynth." It had a rather bitter ground fruit, somewhat like an orange. It was probably a member of the Carrot family, *Ammiaceae,* and was used both as a green herb and a potherb.

Several members of the Gourd family (*Cucurbitaceae*) are mentioned, particularly in the discussion of potherbs or pottage. This family includes pumpkins, many varieties of squash, as well as other edible gourds.

Several kinds of berries, the fruits of true herbs, were common in the food that is mentioned.

Cummin was an herb belonging to the Carrot family (*Ammiaceae*). This plant, *Cuminum cyminum,* had fennel-like leaves and its seeds were used as a condiment. It is mentioned in the Bible as subject to tithe; also, in Ezekiel 4:9, "Take thou also unto thee wheat, and barley, and beans and lentiles, and millet, and fitches . . . , and make thee bread thereof, ..." The "fitches" was another name for a black variety of cummin, sometimes called "vetch."

In Isaiah 28:25, we read: "When he hath made plain the face thereof, doth he not cast abroad the fitches, and scatter the cummin, and cast in the principal wheat, and the ap-

pointed barley and the rie in their place?" The "rie" referred
to was the cereal we know as rye. It was native to Palestine
and the lands to north and east.

It was threshed by staff and flail, or perhaps by a toothed
implement drawn over the mass by oxen. Then the mass
was "winnowed," thrown into the air for the wind to blow
the chaff away. The ancient harvesters sifted the grain and
ground it into flour. The grinding mill consisted of two
circular stones, each about two feet in diameter. The grain
was poured into a central hole in the top stone. This top
was rotated by hand. The crudely crushed grain was
pushed out around the sides and collected in cloths. It was
baked into a rather inferior kind of bread.

The small bushy herb called RUE (*Ruta graveolens*)
was very valuable in the life of the ancient people of
Palestine. It was used in cookery and medicine, and was
subject to the Law of Tithing. It is mentioned only once in
the Bible. In Luke 11:42, we read, "But woe unto you,
Pharisees! for ye tithe mint and rue and all manner of
herbs, and pass over judgment and the love of God: These
ought ye to have done, and not to leave the other undone."

The specific name, "graveolens" means "strong smelling."
It was widely used as a disinfectant, and also as a flavoring
in foods, but it was highly prized also for its medicinal
properties.

A small annual herb with noteworthy habits of growth
was abundant on the shores of the Dead Sea in the Holy
Land. It was considered sacred by the early people, as
representing the Resurrection. The common name was The

Rose of Jericho. Its botanical name is *Anastatica hiero-chuntica*. It is referred to in the Bible as "A Rolling thing," (Isaiah 17:13) because of its characteristic habits. When dry, it will roll up into a ball, and apparently be dead. When the wind took it, it would be scattered over a wide area. Then when it received a little moisture, it would open up, flat on the ground, and take root again, producing tiny, delicate flowers and green leaves. This characteristic has given it the name, "The Resurrection Flower."

While the dictionary gives the definition of a "mandrake" as "a poisonous plant, belonging to the Potato family (Solanaceae), yet in the Bible (Genesis 30:14 and The Song of Solomon 7:13) it apparently was highly prized by the Hebrew people as a charm against evil spirits. It was also thought that it would induce fertility, as in the story of Leah and Rachel.

Galbanum, according to the dictionary, is a bitter and odorous gum resin obtained from certain umbelliferous herbs, especially the giant fennel (*Ferula galbaniflua*). It is used as a stimulant, expectorant, and antispasmodic. Its history, as related to ancient Israel, can best be told by quoting the Biblical reference (Exodus 30:34–37): "And the LORD said unto Moses, Take unto thee sweet spices, stacte, and onycha, and *galbanum;* these sweet spices with pure frankincense: of each shall there be a like *weight:*

"And thou shalt make it a perfume, a confection after the art of the apothecary, tempered together, pure *and* holy.

"And thou shalt beat *some* of it very small, and put of it before the testimony in the tabernacle of the congregation,

51

where I will meet with thee: it shall be unto you most holy.

"And *as for* the perfume which thou shalt make, ye shall not make to yourselves according to the composition thereof: it shall be unto thee holy for the LORD."

The herb from which the gum galbanum is obtained grew from Syria to Persia. It is a fetid, yellowish gum resin. When it is dried and burned, it gives out a pungent but quite pleasant odor. There are nine different species of this herb that grow in the Holy Land. From one of these species (*Ferula assafoetida*) comes our modern evil-smelling gum, assafoetida.

Of the nine species, however, the one which produces the gum, galbanum, seems to be the only one used habitually and religiously by the Israelites. It was collected from cuts made in the young stem a short distance above the ground. The milky juice that exudes soon hardens.

In the 4th chapter of the Song of Solomon, the 13th to 15th verses, we find the following poetical description: "Thy plants *are* an orchard of pomegranates, . . ; campfire, with spikenard.

"Spikenard and saffron; calamus and cinnamon, with all trees of frankincense; myrrh and aloes, with all the chief spices."

The dictionary says of spikenard, "An ancient and fragrant and costly ointment prepared from a plant of the same name: A perennial herb, *Nardostachys jatamansi*, belonging to the valerian family."

In the 14th Chapter of Mark, in the New Testament, the

3rd verse, mention is made of "an alabaster box of ointment of spikenard, very precious."

In very ancient times, the oil derived from this herb was one of the costly treasures of the people around the Mediterranean coasts. One pound was valued at three hundred denarii—a denarius was the equivalent of a laborer's daily wage. The costly oil was carried in alabaster boxes, to preserve the essential perfume.

The SAFFRON referred to in the Biblical account is an autumn-flowering herb, a species of the Crocus family (*Crocus sativus*) which has orange-colored stigmas. These stigmas, when dried, yield a dye which is used today for coloring confectionery and in varnish manufacturing. In ancient days, in Palestine and the Near East, it found wide use in food flavoring, as a condiment, and a delightful odor in exquisite perfumes—these, in addition to its value as a brilliant orange dye in food coloring. In ancient writing, Homer and Theophrastus both mention the saffron flower. Pliny records that costly saffron petals were placed in tiny fountains, that the sweet odor might be diffused into the public halls.

WORMWOOD (*Artemisia judaica* or *Artemisia absinthium*) is mentioned many times in the Bible, and always in connection with its bitterness. In Deuteronomy 29:18, we read, "Lest there should be among you a root that beareth gall and wormwood."

This herb, native to Eastern Europe and Western Asia, is a member of the Thistle family, *Carduaceae,* of the genus

Artemisia, which derives its name from the Greek Goddess ARTEMIS. The leaves have a very bitter taste, and in ancient times the herb was steeped in wine to counteract the effect of the alcohol. It is related to the familiar sagebrush.

The WATER LILY (*Nymphaea caerulea* or *Nymphaea odorata*) was highly prized by the Israelites. When Hiram of Tyre directed the decorations of King Solomon's Temple and the manufacture of the Temple Utensils he used the water lily as a pattern. This flower of the aquatic herb floats on the surface of lakes and pools in the Holy Land, as well as in Egypt. In Nymphaea caerulea the flowers are large, a rich powder blue in color, and extremely fragrant. Nymphaea lotus, of the Nile and also found in California, and the common water lily, Nymphaea odorata, bear white flowers. Because of its beauty, the plant was a great favorite in the gardens of the wealthy. In the rootstocks of this plant there is an abundance of nutritious starchy mucilage and sugary matter. Also, the seeds are filled with a floury nitrogenous albumen. Both seeds and the rootstocks were used as food. In some sections of the land, the blooms of this plant were used as grain and ground into flour, to make bread. Recently the Madonna Lily (*Lilium candidae*) has been identified as also indigenous to Palestine and the Mediterranean lands.

When the early inhabitants of Palestine washed their clothes in the River Jordan, or the Sea of Galilee, or even in the Dead Sea, they discovered that if they mixed the ashes of certain herbs with oil, and used that mixture in their

54

washing, their clothes became much whiter. Thus was the science of soap-making born. The herbs that gave the best results both belong to the Goosefoot family, *Chenopodiaceae*. They are *Salsola kali* and *Salsola inermis*, the common saltworts, and *Salicornia fruticosa* and *Salicornia herbacea*, the common name of which is "Glasswort." These herbs grew in abundance on the shores of the lakes and rivers. Because they burned with an oily flame, they were used as kindling.

In Isaiah 43:24, can be noted a reference to another common herb, "Thou hast brought me no sweet cane with money, . . ." This has been interpreted as the Sugar Cane, *Saccharum officinarum*. The normal sweetening in food of course was honey but the crushed cane was used also, without refining, since the processing for the manufacturing of sugar was unknown until centuries later.

Many herbs of the Thistle family (Carduaceae) were used, either as food or in connection with rituals of worship. Worthy of note is the Star Thistle, of which several varieties were known. Probably the most outstanding examples are *Centaurea cyanus*, with flowers varying in color from blue to rose and white; *Centaurea solstitalis* and *Centaurea calcitrapa*, both with yellow flowers. These grew in waste places, and the seeds were plumose—having fine feathery hairs that blow in the wind, scattering the seeds far and wide.

Other herbs included Chicory (*Chicorium intybus*), Hyacinth, (*Hyacinthus orientalis*) and Water cress (*Nasturtium officinalis.*)

55

PART TWO

FOLKLORE AND TRANSITION

CHAPTER FIVE

"Everything Is Becoming"

ARCHAEOLOGISTS AND STUDENTS OF ANCIENT lore generally agree that the oldest known stone structure is the Ziggurat, or stepped pyramid, planned and erected by Imhotep, chief adviser to King Zoser, of the Third Dynasty in Egypt, approximately 5000 years ago. The encyclopedia says of him: "Imhotep, Egyptian physician, architect and statesman, flourished between approximately 2980 and 2950 B.C. He was chief advisor to King Zoser of the Third Dynasty. Imhotep built the step pyramid, oldest of the Egyptian pyramids, for Zoser. His fame as a physician and scholar grew through the centuries and at the New Kingdom he was deified and worshipped as the god of learning. The Greeks identified Imhotep with Aesculapius, their physician-God."

A Reuter's Despatch from Cairo, in January, 1965, is headed, "SHRINE OF FATHER OF MEDICINE UNEARTHED." It tells of the Egyptian excavations of Professor Walter Emery of London University. Emery says he unearthed a place of worship. He compared it to Lourdes in France as a place where miraculous cures were believed to have taken place, due to Imhotep's influence.

The discovery of his tomb will undoubtedly bring to light ancient inscriptions and documents of enormous scientific value.

Undoubtedly Imhotep's extensive activities had much to do with the early use of herbs and herbal products, since legend, folklore, and early records attribute the advance in medical science and practice to the healing qualities of herbs.

Imhotep's life and work have been compared to that of Leonardo da Vinci (1452–1519), who was equally adept as an artist, sculptor, engineer, architect, super-scientist, and statesman. There are many parallels between the two men. (The Rosicrucian Egyptian Museum in San Jose, California, has a splendid large model of King Zoser's pyramid and the sacred precincts, or city, in which it was contained. The city, now called Sâkkara, was the first stone one in Egypt.)

Beginning with the fall of Rome and continuing until the time of the Renaissance—in that period which commonly is called "the Dark Ages"—what is considered culture was at low ebb. Yet despite the apparent decline of higher learning and outstanding examples of advanced thought and accomplishment in the arts and sciences, there was an underlying habit pattern that permeated all classes of society. The developing influence and power of the church undoubtedly had much to do with this.

It is instinctive in all human beings to worship, fear, adore, or placate a being or beings more powerful than themselves. Some form of religion characterizes every society from the lowest savage to the highest in the scale of intelligence, throughout history. The majority of religions have included much ritual in their activities. As has been seen in the Egyptian, Carthaginian, Phoenician, Druidic, and Hebrew practices, herbs played a major role in their ritualism. During the centuries of the Middle Ages, the arts and learning were in the cultural doldrums; not entirely quiescent but certainly not progressively active.

Commerce and trade were active, and conquest and petty wars were not uncommon. The people still needed food, and the use of herbs increased rather than diminished. One phase in their use was an advance. That was most noticeable in Western Europe among the Gauls, in what later became France. Undoubtedly the druidic influence was primarily responsible.

In their use of herbs, the properties of the individual plants determined the particular application of the herb, whether in votive offering, in medicinal use, or in food. This was based partially on tradition and folklore, and partly on experience and observation. The Romans and Greeks had adopted a similar practice in a somewhat limited manner, but it was the Gauls and early French who really developed the idea into a semblance of scientific accuracy. This laid the groundwork for the modern science and art of perfume manufacturing, in which France has taken the lead.

It must be understood, however, that progress along that line was necessarily slow. There were no scientific standards by which to judge. Individual opinion, based partially on legend and also on personal observation, was called upon to determine the properties of the various herbs. Truly it was "trial and error."

There is a widely accepted psychological theory that no two individuals react identically to any sense perception. In other words, whether it be visual, auditory, gustatory, tactile, or olfactory, one person will have a different interpretation than others. An interesting experiment was conducted in a University class recently. Ten students were selected by lot, blindfolded, and taken into an anteroom. An object was selected and each student was brought into the room and told to smell the unknown substance and immediately write his or her first reaction. There were ten different answers. "Fruity," "sweet," "heady," "strong," "rosy," "nice," "sexual," "unpleasant," "delightful," and "lovely." Then the blindfolds were removed. The object smelled was a small imported sample of Bulgarian Rose Otto. Other odors were tried, with equally amazing results. The logical conclusion is that it is not safe to rely on one person's reaction, especially if one sense perception only is involved.

Two people may watch the same scene. Each will interpret it differently. The same applies to smell, taste, hearing, and feeling. True research in scientific achievement is based on a long series of experimentation. The transitional years in Western Europe exemplify this.

There is an old proverb: "Make haste slowly." Any worthwhile accomplishment is the result of an idea, plus thought, plus development that usually entails discarding unsuccessful attempts, until finally the fruition results and "something new" greets the public eye. Numerous examples can be given. Electric power, railroads, telephones, telegraph, radio, television, various modern electronic devices—none of these came into being suddenly, without previous effort, sometimes years of disappointment. When Henry Ford first had the idea of a "horseless carriage," people ridiculed him. Persistence, faith, and determination have given us our modern transportation facilities.

For at least one hundred years before the Fall of Rome in A.D. 476–478, learning and the arts had been eclipsed by wars, rumors of wars, and internal politics. Invasions from the north and west, petty jealousies among the ruling classes, frequent changes in government in Rome precluded attention to the higher aspects of life. There were a few individuals, however, both in Rome itself and in the territory of the Franks and Gauls, and in the disputed country between the North Sea and the Iberian Peninsula, whose ideals were creative and constructive. Despite popular discouragements they planted the seeds that bore fruit in the rebirth of scientific achievement, literature, and the arts.

So accustomed are we in our modern, busy life to accept as "good" what other people proclaim as worthwhile that it sometimes is difficult to realize that it is not the "me, too" type of person who makes progress.

One result of applied thought during the Dark Ages was the increasing use of medicinal herbs for healing. Another was the expanding use of herbs and herbal products for their emotional effect, which has resulted in our modern gigantic perfume and cosmetic industry.

The increase in the medicinal use of herbs during this period is evidenced by folklore and legend, as well as by the customs of the early colonists who came to America during the two centuries after the beginning of the Renaissance from France, Spain, Italy, and England. The knowledge of "folk remedies" in the early days of the American Colonies was extensive and was not confined to a particular region. The similarity in the use of herbs and herbal products for their healing properties, from New England and the Atlantic coast and in the French settlements in Louisiana, indicates a common origin for the practices which these colonists brought with them. England, Germany, the Rhine countries, France, Spain, and Italy were the original homes of the settlers. It is logical to believe, therefore, that during the centuries before the revival of learning this phase of herbal application received especial attention in Europe.

It is even psychologically conceivable that because of the preponderance of wars and rumors of wars the curative power of growing plants was recognized and used. That is pure conjecture, of course, but it is a possible factor.

Artifacts have been found in caves attributed to the Cro-Magnon era that undoubtedly were used to contain perfumery or cosmetics. During the centuries the contents had evaporated, of course, but a slight odor remained in the flacons. Excavators have discovered the same situation in the earliest tombs of the Egyptian Pharaohs. The use of perfumes and cosmetics antedates historical records.

It must be understood, however, that these early examples of the perfumers' art were not the elaborate bouquets and blended odors of the present time. According to literature and research, perfumery in the beginning was the concentrated essence of one flower—a rose, or some other blossom. That condition existed until nearly A.D. 500.

Two of the earliest mentioned odors, in the records of the Bible and other ancient writings, are frankincense and myrrh. Neither of these are herbs or herbal products. Sometimes frankincense is referred to as galibanum. Both of these substances are resinous gums exuding from trees. They were used extensively in incense and as offerings to the gods, and later incorporated in perfumery as it developed.

The transition from the use of frankincense and myrrh to the addition of the floral odors was a natural accompaniment to the increasing sense of the aesthetic or higher emotions. Probably the first flower to be used and cultivated for its pleasing odor was the Damask Rose, which traditionally originated in Damascus. Undoubtedly an aromatic gum resin was the host, on the surface of which successive layers of the petals were pressed and allowed to remain for some time. The host gradually absorbed the essential oil from the flowers, and a pleasing substance was obtained. The "pomades" were produced in this fashion for many years before liquid perfumery was developed.

No definite records have been discovered that show the

exact date when the different flower odors began to be mixed and blended to form a bouquet. However, it is assumed that this natural transition originated in Italy, although some of the modern "bouquets" have names that suggest an Arabian, or Phoenician, or Greek beginning. For example, the well-known commercial odor sold under the name, FRENCH CHYPRE, may be a combination of as many as twenty-four odors, in various percentages, but all of the formulae have the predominating odor of two ingredients—OAKMOSS and BERGAMOT. The name *Chypre* suggests the Island of Cyprus, while BERGAMOT is a derivative of the American HORSEMINT, *Monarda menthaefolia.*

Prior to A.D. 1300, probably there was no alcoholic solution of essential oils to make perfumes as we know them today. The sweet odors were "captured" and held by various aromatic gums such as frankincense and myrrh, or natural oils which had a pleasing odor and which would also blend with the flower essence. Many of these oils were also used for medicinal purposes by the ancient people. These applications are mentioned by eminent historical writers such as Pliny and Ovid.

Available evidence proves that the earliest method used to gather the aromatic oils from the flowers or plants, as well as the least expensive, is the process known as steam distillation. Artifacts from ancient Egypt have been identified as crude stills.

It is well known that a substance can exist in one of three different states: solid, liquid, or gas. The most familiar

66

example is water. When the temperature falls below zero degrees Centigrade or thirty-two degrees Fahrenheit, we have ice, a solid. Between zero degrees and 100 degrees Centigrade, or 32 and 212 Fahrenheit, water is a liquid— that is, the molecular pressure is increasing, but still not sufficient to overcome the surface tension, or cohesion. But at the "boiling point" the internal molecular activity becomes greater than the tension, and the liquid becomes vapor. So it is with the essential flower oils.

Many oils have higher "boiling points" than water. Therefore, they would require greater heat application to vaporize. By introducing water or steam into the alembic, or container, the required amount of heat is lowered. The vapor, consisting of mixed steam and flower oil gas, is re-condensed to liquid usually by a coil of cold water surrounding the exit tube. This is illustrated by the diagram that follows.

Into this container flowers were placed, heat was applied at the bottom, and steam was introduced at the top "X". The combined heat "C" and steam vaporized the essential

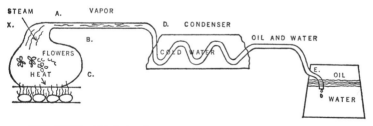

"A" THE ALEMBIC, OR DISTILLING APPARATUS

67

oils in the flowers, which "escaped" through the tube "B" into the coil "D" immersed in cold water. This condensed the vapor of the oils and steam, which then went over into the container "E." Because oil is lighter than water, the oil floated on top and was drawn off and further purified.

The very early historical references indicate that this steam distillation method was used, along with the pomades and natural blends with aromatic gums. The exact date for the beginning use of alcohol as the "absorbent vehicle" for the flower oils is not known, but indications are that it probably was in the early 1300's, undoubtedly in Italy. It was soon after that time when the blending of mixed odors, or bouquets, began to be practiced.

When Catherine de Medici came to France to marry Henri II, early in the sixteenth century, she was accompanied by her private professional cosmetician, a young man named René, an expert in the art of perfumery and cosmetics. As Patron Saint of the art of fragrance in France, Catherine de Medici is credited with the encouragement of the cultivation of vast gardens of flowers for profitable production of essential oils for the manufacture of perfumes on an increasingly large scale. Her sponsorship of the "infant industry" was the beginning of the development which has made France undoubted leader in the science and art of perfume manufacturing in the modern world.

In their search for the elixir of life and the philosopher's stone, it was not long until the alchemists began to experiment with various flowers, herbs, and herbal products. Alchemy has often been called the prelude to chemistry, which is a universal science—science is an orderly, systematic pursuit of knowledge. When the art of perfumery began to be studied in an orderly, systematic manner, it took its rightful place in the forefront of scientific achievement. This was not confined to France alone. The effect was noticeable in Switzerland, Germany, Italy, Greece, England, Spain, and the lands surrounding the Mediterranean. The study of herbs and herbal products for their emotional effect as well as for their commercial and medicinal values undoubtedly marked the beginning of the widespread appreciation of herbalism and its function in every phase of our modern life.

Early in the nineteenth century, Cologne came to the attention of the public. It was named after the city in Germany which originated it. At that time, an attempt was made to shift the center of the industry from France to Germany, but because of the ideal climatic conditions in southern France the move was not successful.

The number of plants that can be classified and described as herbs seems almost endless. All of the cereal grains are seeds of herbs. The majority of the familiar vegetables are herbs. Many plants from which medicinal values are derived belong to the group. To attempt to list and describe all members of this vast assembly would require many volumes. In references to herbs in the Bible, it is evident that at those times all green plants were considered herbs, regardless of their woody fiber. If we eliminate the growths that show woody content in the stems, the number is still stupendous.

Civilization in the past as well as the so-called culture of today was dependent upon an unfailing supply of plants as the source of food. Modern, thinking people are becoming increasingly aware of the importance of herbs, not only as potential nourishment but in other ways as well. For the purpose of study and understanding, herbs can be classified in three main categories. The largest group would be those which are used or can be utilized as food. Another division includes the plants whose primary importance is determined by properties valuable in the healing arts, in medicine. The third list embraces the herbs, mostly flowering plants, that furnish the source of the essential oils for the gigantic perfume industry. Individual species of herbs are not always confined to one group. Overlapping is common. A single plant or botanical family may be good for food, may also have medicinal value, and rate high in perfume oils as well.

In addition to the above grouping, possibly another classification might be mentioned. Certain herbs or species are poisonous or otherwise dangerous to human welfare. An example is the opium poppy as contrasted with the related species that furnishes seeds used to decorate foods. The opium poppy is *Papaver somniferus.* The seed poppy is *Papaver rhoeas.*

Another example is the mandrake, *Atropa mandragora,* which was mentioned in the Bible and was valued for its delightful odor, particularly of its fruit. Also it was prized for the romantic medicinal properties. In the Bible story of

70

Rachel and Leah the romance of its healing power is related.

Flax is an herb with a multiplicity of uses. The finest of linen is made from its fibers, and the seeds are used in the manufacture of paints and varnishes, and also linseed for various medicinal values. There is a definite amount of food value also.

Referring to the mandrake again, the name was given because of a fancied resemblance of the root to a man with his arms outstretched. In the eastern countries, in the early days, it was thought that if a man dug up a mandrake plant he would die! So they harnessed a dog to the plant and let the animal pull it up. It was not reported whether the animal died or not.

There are several species of mandrake. The most noteworthy variety, *Mandragora officinarum,* bears fruits which resemble a small tomato, red to pale orange when ripe. The odor is delightful.

According to Pliny, mandrake root was considered as an anaesthetic, which was a humane touch in the strenuous life in Roman times. A piece of the root was to be chewed by a patient while undergoing an operation. Medicinally, the entire plant was thought to promote restful sleep, to ease pain. Also it was helpful in diseases of the mind, and in Anglo-Saxon folklore it was a specific remedy against evil spirits and demons. Even today the leaves are occasionally used to prepare ointments to be used externally. The roots have emetic properties.

An interesting commentary on the development of herbal use during the Middle Ages is contained in Culpepper's book, *The English Physician and Herbalist,* published about 1653. His belief in what he called "The Doctrine of Signatures" was ridiculed by his contemporaries. This theory stipulated that the appearance or image of every herb determined its use by man. That was a development of the thought processes that really led up to the scientific study of herbs and herbal products.

His explanations and descriptions apparently are based on the great influence of the planetary constellations under which all herbs apparently are protected. His conclusions were that the herb itself would tell by its form, its leaves, its inflorescence, of what value or use it would be to man as a cure for human ailments. For example, the crossed petals of plants in the Family *Cruciferae* reassure man that it is not poisonous or harmful. The lungwort's spotted leaves indicate that it is a beneficial plant for treatment of spotted or diseased lungs. Dandelion, buttercup, and "butter-and-eggs" were good in treatment of jaundice. Garlic, with its hollow stalk, is useful in affections of the windpipe. Solomon's Seal, *Polygonatum biflorum,* has seallike scars on its rootstalk. His comment: "Root excellent. Good for to close up wounds, broken bones, and such like. It soldereth and glues together bones in a very short space of time though the bones be but slenderly and unhandsomely placed and wrapped up."

Many other herbs and plants are listed according to their

"images." The majority of his conclusions have been verified by modern practices. Dandelion, plantain, nettles, and yarrow, for example, have been found to have merit in the healing art. The study of these applications is fascinating and self-rewarding. Truly, "Everything is becoming."

CHAPTER SIX

Herbs in the Colonies

FROM ENGLAND, FRANCE, IRELAND, SCOTLAND, Germany, Austria, Sweden and Norway, Holland, and other parts of the old world they came to the land of promise and increased opportunity. The call of curiosity, the summons of adventure, the desire for wealth, the longing for freedom to worship as conscience dictated, all had influence on the motives underlying the westward movements. The theory that "geography is the parent of history" is exemplified in the distribution of the various nationalistic groups in the early colonial settlements in America.

The emigrants from northern France came to the eastern Great Lakes and the Saint Lawrence Valley. The Gulf Region and the lower Mississippi attracted those from southern France and Spain. The northern Great Lakes' lands appealed to many from Sweden, Norway, and Denmark. The Dutch, Scottish, and Irish settled in the Hudson Valley and Eastern seaboard. Those from Germany preferred the hills of Pennsylvania. The English, with characteristic ambition, were not content with one location but mingled with all, even occasionally outnumbering the original settlers. Each group retained their own folklore and traditions, especially those regarding the use of herbs as food and for medicinal and healing purposes.

Many of the herbs that grew wild in the new land were similar to the familiar ones back in their homeland, and these were used and cultivated immediately. Others were new to the settlers, so they became experimental material. In addition, many of the immigrants brought with them the seeds of their favorite plants, especially those that had been cultivated for their healing properties. Their herb gardens, planted near their homes, were sources of useful plants and those of medicinal value as well as food.

A few of the plants which they found growing wild and used in their home remedies have found a place in today's folk medicine. Wild ginger roots were similar to their English and North European *asarabacca* and they provided the same medicinal use for easing pains of cramps, and also they were dried and used as snuff. Two varieties of BALMONY (or Turtle Head), (*Chelone glabra* and *Chelone lyoni*) found use in the treatment of jaundice and as a soothing, healing skin ointment. CENTAURY (*Centaurium umbellatum*) was apparently worth its weight in gold as a priceless cure for various ailments.

LABRADOR TEA (*Ledum groenlandicum*) was a fragrant, low-growing herb the leaves of which were used for tea in the Colonial days. It was thought in Colonial times that PURPLE LOOSESTRIFE (*Lythrum salicaria*) was useful and quite effective in relieving the tension of disordered minds! SWEET FLAG (*Acorus calamus*) is an herb with a thick, creeping root used in making the "sweet flag candy" by the Shakers, a religious sect that came from England early in the eighteenth century and settled in New York, with later colonies in New England, Ohio, Indiana, and Kentucky.

PITCHER PLANT (*Sarracenia purpurea*) was (and is) a noted insectivorous plant found mostly in peat bogs. This plant was an old Indian remedy which was thought to prevent pitting from smallpox. Another plant, SUNDEW, (genus *Drosera*) was "death to mosquitoes." Its leaves are covered with sticky tentacles that fold over unwary insects, particularly mosquitoes. All its species are still used in treatment of whooping cough.

It is somewhat surprising to think of the WATER LILY (*Nymphea odorata*) as a medicinal herb, but it was cultivated by the pioneers for its healing qualities.

The common MEADOWSWEET (*Spiraea salicifolia*). In the Shaker colonies this herb was cultivated very much, for use in preparing their "botanic beer" on account of its sweet flavor, which saved sugar. TEASEL, (*Dipsacus fullonum*) is an herb with prickly, recurved spines growing on its beautiful flower heads. These were used to comb velvet. That use explains its European common name—"Brushes and Combs."

The Mallow family (*Malvaceae*), has many representatives, some of which show important medicinal properties. Of these, the most important is the Marsh mallow (*Althaea officinalis*) which yields a soothing, medicinal mucilage which was used, and still is, in the form of a syrup reputed to relieve congestion in the bronchial passages. The common hollyhock, (*Althaea rosea*) is a relative. One of the uses, carried over from colonial days, is for coloring purposes.

The herb commonly known as MARIGOLD (*Calendula officinalis*) was cultivated several centuries ago both for culinary purposes and because of its medicinal properties. The flowers were used in salads, and when dried were also used in soups and broths. A preparation of the entire plant was said to be efficacious as a soothing ointment for ulcers and sores or irritations of the skin.

The MARJORAMS, particularly the SWEET MARJORAM (*Majorana hortensis*), which has been called "Joy of the Mountains," and originally imported from Europe in Colonial times, is still valuable in flavoring foods. It is often mixed with other herbs and used in poultry stuffing, either fresh or dried; also in omelets, salads, and other foods where its warm flavor is especially delightful. The French, English, and Italian varieties were highly prized, as well. The modern appreciation of this herb for its culinary qualities is a heritage from our colonial ancestors.

MEADOWSWEET (*Spiraea ulmaria*) occupied a unique position in herbal application in Colonial days and even before. Undoubtedly it was a native of England or the Continent. In an old English manuscript written by one Gerard, the following statement appears: "The leaves and floures of Meadowsweet arre excelle alle other strowing herbs for to decke up houses . . . for the smell thereof makes the heart merrie and joyful and delighteth the senses." The expression 'strowing herbs' referred to the custom of scattering the flowers and leaves around the rooms of houses to purify the air. It was one of the many herbs venerated by the Druids. An infusion of the dried plant in water was thought to be a remedy for diarrhoea. Culpepper recommends it for pulmonary troubles.

Members of the Mint family were the source of many applications during Colonial times, even as they are today. This family (LABIATAE) is worldwide in distribution. Some 200 genera and 3000 species are known. Some of the most familiar representatives which were used in the Colonies and which have continued to benefit human needs through the years may be listed.

The perfume oil, BERGAMOT, is derived from the American HORSEMINT (*Monarda menthaefolia*). Peppermint oil comes from PEPPERMINT (*Mentha piperita*). The common CATNIP is *Nepeta cataria.* HOARHOUND (*Marrubium vulgare*) is a member of the Mint family. THYME is *Thymus vulgaris.* SAGE (*Salvia*—several species) should not be confused with "Sagebrush," which belongs to the Compositae—genus *Artemisia.* The true SAGE is a member of the Mint family. Also, SKULLCAP (*Scutellaria spp*) and COLEUS (*Coleus spp*). The "spp" means that there are several species. The various examples of the Mints are useful for food embellishment, in medicines, and in the perfume industry.

The Rose family, *Rosaceae,* was well represented in the herbal usage of the American colonists. This is a rather large family, numbering 70 genera and 1200 species. It has worldwide distribution, but only about one fourth are common in the United States. Some familiar representatives, in addition to the true roses, are raspberries, strawberries, the cinquefoil, or *Potentilla* group, buttercups, and numerous others. Many of our roses today are later imports. For example, it was not until 1810 that the Tea Rose was imported into France from China, since when it has become the progenitor of many of our exquisite modern roses.

Red roses are usually considered to be the most fragrant, today as they were in Colonial times. Pink flowers came next, while yellow blossoms although beautiful in appearance were the least fragrant. It is reported that experienced rosarians, both in the olden days and in modern times, are able to tell the different types of roses in the dark. But it also is significant that no two blossoms, even on the same plant, are exactly identical in odor! That raises the natural question, just what causes the odor in a flower? Is it the essential oils from the petals? Do the odors from the leaves affect the total aroma? Does the variation in odor of different flowers on the same plant depend on the percentage of the aromatic source in the individual blossom? Interesting research is suggested.

Some interesting facts have been gleaned from legend, folklore, and early records.* For example, rose perfume has long been thought to have curative powers. The damask rose is supposed to be the best and most highly esteemed

* (The Rose has long been a symbol of mystical philosophy. Its tradition in this regard is perpetuated by the Rosicrucian Order, AMORC.)

80

for the manufacture of rose water. Roses kept in a room will insure that the air will be purified, sweet, and clean. Leaves hold their perfume longer than flowers, particularly when dried. Leaf odors are nearly all stimulating and quite refreshing. Since green plants "breathe" through their leaves, the air in a room is purified if green plants are present. In photosynthesis, the chlorophyll—the green coloring matter of vegetable organisms—acts as the controlling factor in plant metabolism. Carbon dioxide is taken from the air to combine with water and form starch, with oxygen as the "by-product" of the reaction.

Modern study and research have verified many of the early beliefs and practices of our ancestors in the Colonial days which were largely based on tradition and folklore. One of the principles on which early folk medicine was based is that Nature created the body ideally, in perfect balance; that sickness is the result of interference with that balanced condition; that ill health is the road sign that tells us we have wandered away from proper nourishment of our physical being. The answer to that was the return to Nature's food supply: the use of herbs to furnish the elements that would restore the balanced relation of the various bodily activities.

To a large extent, the modern health food development is an outgrowth of an idea. The food which we eat is the determining cause of good health or illness; of mental and bodily strength or weakness; of hope and ambition or discouragement. In other words, we *are* what we eat. There is more truth than fiction in that statement. The historical

81

study of mankind reveals that the strongest and most progressive people were those whose eating habits were the simplest. The use of herbs as food antedates and dominates the gustatory customs of all nations.

In studying the folklore of various population groups in the early settlement of America, it is interesting to note what might be called a geographical similarity in the use of herbs as food.

Folk customs, particularly in relation to health and the treatment of disease, seem to have followed the pattern of "Three R's"—RESISTANCE, REPAIR, and RECOVERY. This was especially true in the northeastern colonies, Maine, New Hampshire, Vermont, Connecticut, Massachusetts, and Rhode Island. Whether this was because of racial instinct, tradition, or experience, or possibly a combination of these factors, or by reason of a natural craving, their basic food was cereals—which are the seeds of herbs—and other herbal products such as honey, various vegetables and fruits, many of which may be classified as true herbs.

Before the use of refined sugar as a sweetening agent, honey was the oustanding natural sweet. In addition to its carbohydrate content, it is the only substance that offers many life-giving qualities not found in combination elsewhere. As such, it meets the requirements as a RESISTANCE builder, a REPAIR agent, and a RECOVERY product.

It is readily understood that the pioneer settlers in any region must build minds and bodies that will resist the dangers that surround them. The use of honey will not perform miracles, of course, but it has definite properties that work together to build the desired qualities. It does not irritate the lining of the digestive tract. It is assimilated rapidly and with ease. As a source of quick energy it is ideal. Its use facilitates rapid recovery after exertion. It offers no strain on the kidneys. It is a natural and gentle laxative. It appears to quiet the nerves. It is not difficult to obtain and relatively inexpensive. For these and other reasons, honey as an herbal product was included in the food supply in the majority of the Colonies. Yet even more important in the lives of the pioneers were its medicinal properties.

According to reports from many physicians and from government publications and university researches, honey has definite bactericidal properties. It is reputed to have a soothing, healing effect on the throat and bronchial passages, and to be a general body conditioner.

The common POTATO has an interesting history. Contrary to popular belief, it did not originate in Ireland. This staple of diet (*Solanum tuberosum*) is a native of the Andean countries, in South America. The name *potato* originally was derived from the Haitian word *batata* which was changed to the Spanish *patata* and ultimately to the English POTATO. It has been reported that a Franciscan priest, with the Pizarro exploring expedition, brought potato plants back to Spain with him in 1534. There, it was hailed as a miracle plant, able to revitalize impotence. The price of the "earth-berries" soared, according to legend, often reaching more than 1000 pesos per pound! It is reported that Sir John Hawkins brought potato plants to Ireland in 1565. It was not until 1719, according to the records, that a group of Presbyterian emigrants from Ireland brought potatoes to America, settling in New York and Massachusetts. That is why the earth-berries are popularly known as "Irish Potatoes." They are the rootstalks of the true herb, *Solanum tuberosum.* After their importation, they became a definite part of the food of the colonists.

Because our national motto, "E PLURIBUS UNUM," means *one out of many* it is not surprising that the eating habits of the American people are a combination of the national customs of the different countries from which the pioneer settlers came. One of the favorites in the early days was mint tea. According to ancient beliefs, it was a remedy for colic, upset stomach, nausea, chills, colds, etc. Modern analysis proves that it is high in Vitamin C. It can be made from dried mint.

In addition to the use of cereal grains and other herbal products as food, there were certain medicinal characteristics attributed to many herbs, some of which were used as food and others valued for their healing properties. Many of them played a dual role—both food and medicine. The "folk medicine" in all the colonies showed many similarities, including the examples which have persisted up to the present time, some of which have been incorporated into modern remedies.

It is reported that BALMONY, which is commonly called "Turtle Head," was highly thought of as an herb that would ameliorate the symptoms of jaundice. The leaves of the red

84

variety of Turtle Head were used in an infusion that made a healing ointment for the skin. This use was not confined to a particular colony but apparently was universal. There were two common species: *Chelone glabra* and *Chelone lyoni.*

Blue VERVAIN, belonging to the family *Verbenaceae,* was considered to have value as a "tonic" herb, in addition to its sweet odor.

An infusion of GOAT'S RUE was used to produce abundant perspiration or sweating to relieve high fevers.

The pulverized root of GOLDEN SEAL was a standard remedy to relieve inflammation in certain types of ulcers or other sores. It is still cultivated for its medicinal properties.

The herb called BLOODROOT was efficacious for bronchial trouble, according to reports.

The use of PARTRIDGE BERRY (often called SQUAW BERRY) to relax muscular tension was adopted from Indian folklore. Various tribes used it for that purpose and also to relieve labor pains in childbirth.

Wild THYME tea was said to ease headache, soothe the nerves, and settle upset stomach. It was used by pioneers in the northern Catskills and by settlers in Pennsylvania.

Another member of the Mint family, the familiar LAVENDER (*Lavandula officinalis*) occupied a major place in the herbal economy of the early and later Colonial days. This herb was undoubtedly a native of the Mediterranean countries and during the Middle Ages and the Renaissance it was a prime favorite because of its delightful odor. It has greenish grey foliage and spikes of small, light-purple flowers, which were especially favored for scenting linens. It yields an aromatic oil used in perfumery. It was introduced in the American colonies by the French settlers in the Gulf region, Louisiana and the lower Mississippi, and in the northern area of the St. Lawrence Valley. Its popularity spread rapidly to the other colonies and it became one of the most widely cultivated of all flowering herbs. Oil of lavender is still one of the most highly prized of the perfume-building essences.

In addition to its value in perfumery, some early authorities credit lavender with medicinal qualities. It was said to be effective against apoplexy, palsy, and loss of speech! A mixture of lavender flowers, marjoram, cloves, pinks, betony, and rose leaves and petals, placed in a small bag and worn around the neck, was supposed to cure headache!

Of course ONIONS (*Allium cepa*) and GARLIC (*Allium sativum*) were in practically universal use in the early days, as they are today. Garlic was also used medicinally as a syrup to relieve asthma. It reputedly was mixed with honey for that purpose. Externally it was prepared as an antiseptic poultice for wounds and abrasions.

In addition to its use as a condiment, MUSTARD soon found a place in the Colonies for its counter-irritant properties as a poultice in treating certain diseases. Botanically, MUSTARD is *Brassica nigra*. It has been found in a wild state and cultivated since Biblical times.

Both watermelons and the various varieties of muskmelons and gourds were grown and used in the early settlements. Some of these were native while others were brought to America by the pioneers. The watermelon, for example (*Citrullus vulgaris*), has long been one of the staple articles of food in the Mediterranean countries. It grows abundantly along the banks of the Nile and in Palestine. It was imported into the United States in the early days by the French and Spanish settlers in the Southern States, and today the Gulf States and Texas are the largest producers of the delightful fruit.

The entire GOURD family (*Cucurbitaceae*) includes about 100 genera and 800 species. Watermelons, muskmelons, cantaloupes, pumpkins, squashes, cucumbers, the familiar gourds such as zucchini, are all members of this family of true herbs. From the very early days they have been used for food, and certain varieties of gourds have also been utilized as containers for water and foods.

The largest family among flowering plants, the *Compositae,* was well represented in the Colonies. It is the SUNFLOWER family, and it includes about 1000 genera and 20,000 species, which are found nearly everywhere land plants grow. Some of these herbs are valued as food, such as lettuce, salsify, artichoke, even the sunflower and dandelion, and many others. Chrysanthemums, dahlias, asters, daisies, are examples of those which were valued chiefly as decorations for their flowers. The pollen of a few is reputed to cause hay fever—ragweed, sagebrush, etc. A few, such as snakeroot, are poisonous to livestock. Included in this group were some of the most troublesome weeds that bothered farmers and gardeners in the old Colony days, as well as today. Examples were cockleburs,

87

Canada Thistle, yarrow, Spanish needle, ironweed, and others.

Labrador tea (*Ledum groenlandicum*), a fragrant, low-growing shrubby herb, was apparently native to the country from the New England States north and west. This plant was highly prized by the colonists, who used its leaves to make tea during Revolutionary days, particularly after the protest to imported English tea which was recorded as "The Boston Tea Party."

John Bartram's botanic garden near Philadelphia was reputedly founded in 1730. Its interesting records read almost like adventure fiction in the story of the tireless plant explorers and scientific gardeners who defied discouragement in order that they might bring into being and duplicate many of the beneficial herbs that grew only in the wilds. Some very interesting comments on the daily life of the colonists are recorded in the book, *Peter Kalm's Travels in North America,* by A. D. Benson, published in 1750.

A study of the folklore, folk medicine, legends, and historical records of the early American colonies reveals that in our modern acceptance of the benefits of herbs and herbal products we are utilizing the combined knowledge and customs of the people of many nationalities who flocked to the shores of America, the Land of Opportunity. In every part of America today, there is evidence that the original settlers brought with them the customs and habits of their ancestors. While these have been modified to some degree by time and environment, there is a predominating uniformity in the use of herbs and herbal products in foods and folk medicine, regardless of the nationalistic background of the people. Modern scientific knowledge is recognizing the value of the contributions to healthful living that the pioneer fathers bequeathed to us.

CHAPTER SEVEN

Indian Culture Regions

ARCHAEOLOGISTS AND ANTHROPOLOGISTS ARE
still endeavoring to solve the problem of the ancestry of the
American Indians. Many theories have been advanced.
Some authorities hold to the idea that the red men in North
America are descendants of the original mound builders,
whose artifacts are prominent along the valley of the Ohio
River. However, the origin of the mound builders them-
selves is still an unsolved secret, as is also the question,
"What became of them?"

Today, it is universally accepted that man (*Homo sapiens*) was not the result of a separate act of creation: that
he evolved from simpler forms of animal life. Zoologically,
man's nearest relatives—the anthropoid apes, are all found
in Europe, Asia, and Africa. The platyrrhine monkeys of
South and Central America are more distant from man
biologically than those of the Old World, and they apparently could not have been the ancestors of the American
Indians. Ethnologically it seems certain that the Indians
originated from a race or races of anthropoid creatures who
came to America from Eurasia or Australia after they had

developed the characteristics of Homo sapiens. No "Missing Link" skeletons have been found in America, up to the present time. There is ample evidence, from archaeological explorations, that indicates man's presence in North America 11,000 or 12,000 years ago. From whence did he come, and by what route did he arrive in North America?

When any problem affecting the history and/or welfare of the human race presents itself, many brilliant minds begin to offer suggested solutions. Evidences are adduced from Geology, Paleontology, Zoology, Botany, Archaeology, Ethnology, and even Religion. From the mass of data that has been gathered, certain theories have developed, none of which is capable of one hundred percent proof of accuracy.

Probably the most widely accepted theory is that the ancestors of the Indians entered North America from Asia (Siberia) via Bering Strait at the time of the last recession of ice in the Pleistocene period. From geological studies, it seems probable that land bridges connected Asia and Alaska perhaps several times during the thousands of years when the continental glacier was dwindling. If the Paleo-Indians entered Alaska by this route, they probably did not come in a sudden rush of immigration. They could not have known what conditions awaited them to the south and east. Geologists have estimated that the continental ice-cap probably was hundreds of feet in thickness. To say that the widespread presence of the Indians in North America was the result of this infiltration alone would be highly questionable.

Another theory propounded by some authorities is that the Indians of the Southwest, Mexico, and Central America have descended from South Pacific ancestors; that a similarity of physical traits and customs apparently indicates the truth of this supposition. While this could account for certain factors in the Paleo-Indian life, it still leaves many questions unsolved. For instance, how did they get here? At the time of the original settlement of North America, navigation and sea travel over the great distance from the South Sea islands could not have been probable, or even possible.

Some philosophical thinkers have advanced the idea that the "Lost Continents of Atlantis and Lemuria" provided a land bridge that extended from Africa, through Central and South America, and included Easter Island and Hawaii and the Marquesas group. Their arguments mention the ziggurats, or stepped pyramids, found only in Peru, Bolivia, Central America, and Egypt and Mesopotamia, and the grotesque statues of Easter Island and the South Sea group. Fanciful? Perhaps. Not capable of proof at the present time.

Certain religious groups have assumed that the Paleo-Indians are the descendants of the Lost Tribes of the House of Israel. There is no evidence in the Bible to substantiate the idea of a mass migration during Old Testament times and, even if it were so, it would be much too late to account for the widespread populating of North America.

The theory of "Continental Drift" has been suggested to

account for the supposition that former continents once existed where oceans are today. According to this belief, North America and South America were joined to Europe and Africa, millions of years ago, forming a solid land surface. An old geological name for this "continent" was Gondwanaland. Then, as the earth cooled and shrunk, a cleavage appeared and the surface land separated and drifted apart. The difficulty is that the action took place long before man had evolved, zoologically.

However they came, whatever their ancestry, the Paleo-Indians inhabited North and South America continuously for at least 11,000 to probably more than 20,000 years, before the so-called discovery of the Western Continent by Columbus in 1492. Any changes in their customs and general economy of life before that time undoubtedly were gradual and a matter of adaptation to environment. A reconstructed picture of life at that time will illustrate the truth that geography is the parent of history.

The first people who entered North America, fifteen or twenty thousand years ago, found an arctic climate, unsuited to agriculture and with a minimum of edible wild plants. Undoubtedly they lived largely by hunting and fishing. As they gradually drifted southward, conditions changed. Game was not so plentiful. Fishing was more restricted, but wild, edible plants were more abundant. This changing geographical environment brought about a radical change in the daily life-habits of these early people.

How can we tell the approximate dates of these prehistoric events? Many suggestions have been advanced, the majority of which have proved to be entirely unsatisfactory. There is one method, however, based on scientific fact, which undoubtedly gives accurate results. That is called the radiocarbon test.

Ordinary carbon is an element with an atomic weight of 12. One out of every trillion carbon atoms is radioactive, and this radioactive carbon has an atomic weight of 14. It is present in the infinitesimal amount in each cell of every living organism, both plant and animal. Though small in amount, physicists have been able to measure it. The ratio does not vary during the life of the plant or animal. At death, however, this carbon 14 gradually diminishes. Scientists have estimated that 5760 years after death the amount of the radioactivity will be one half of the original, and that 11,520 years gives a ratio of one fourth. By measuring the carbon 14 remaining in charred wood, etc., from ancient campfires and artifacts from archaeological excavations attributed to the Paleo-Indians, the tentative dates have been computed.

According to estimates, the first major change in the Paleo-Indian life economy began about 11,000 or 12,000 years ago, when environmental conditions forced him to add wild plants and seeds to his diet, instead of relying exclusively on hunting and fishing for his food. Then about two thousand years later, particularly in the West and Southwest, he began to cultivate the wild herbs for himself, thus adding to his food supply.

According to estimates of researchers, substantiated by the radiocarbon method, actual agriculture began in two major sections of North America about nine thousand to ten thousand years ago. These locations were the tropical regions in Central America (plus some evidence in northern South America), and also in the more temperate uplands in Mexico. Excavations in caves have brought to light plant remains, definitely identified as gourds (*Lagemaria ciceraria*) and squash (*Cucurbita pepo* and *Cucurbita foetidissima*). These two undoubtedly were cultivated. Other plant remains in the same caves included a species of Jack beans (*Convalleria ensiformis*) which was probably a wild plant. These discoveries, tested by the radiocarbon standards, give dates between 7000 and 5500 B.C. Evidence has been found also to show that maize (corn) was cultivated in Mexico as early as 4000 B.C.

When the Paleo-Indians began to lead an increasingly agricultural life, more and more herbs were planted, both for food and for their medicinal value. The tribal sachems were even more powerful than the chiefs, for they directed the ritualistic and religious life of the people and were the "medicine men" who were to use their herbal knowledge for health-giving and healing.

Some of the herbal foods cultivated by the Indians contained poisonous material that had to be removed before it could be used as food. That meant experimentation, because all knowledge came through the medicine men; the Indians had no writing, and communication was by word of mouth. It required many years, even centuries, to establish the food habits the colonists found among the Indians after 1492. In general, food habits can be correlated to geographical environment, at least to a large extent.

Looking at the continent of North America from the Arctic to the Isthmus of Panama, there are well-defined zones that show differences in topography, climate, soils, animal life, and plant life even today with modern methods of commerce and communication. Before the white men came during the years following 1492, the distinction was still greater. Of course, the food habits of the Indians varied with the environmental and geographical pattern. These differences may be grouped and correlated by considering the dominance in the daily food ration of fish and game, wild plants, cultivated plants, or a combination of these.

As would be expected, fish was the principal food among the early inhabitants of the Northwest Coast and parts of Alaska and the territory around interior lakes in Canada. Also in the Sault-Sainte-Marie district at the junction of Lakes Superior and Huron and Michigan and on Long Island, the Paleo-Indians were fish eaters, primarily. The tribes living along the northern Gulf Coast, in what is now Louisiana, Mississippi, Alabama, and the Gulf Coast and southern tip of Florida, were generally fish eaters. Even today, Louisiana's advertising slogan is, "A fisherman's paradise!"

In the large wedge-shaped area that included most of the Arctic region, the northern Great Plains country in the United States, and the eastern Rocky Mountains, extending

97

as far south as Texas, game was abundant, and the Indians lived predominantly by hunting. In a few more or less isolated areas in this vast triangle, there is evidence that the people had developed semipermanent camp sites and were subsisting on cultivated herbs. There are two possible explanations for this. One is that wild game in those particular locations was becoming relatively scarce and in order to escape famine they adopted the alternative of farming. Another solution, even more plausible, is part of the folklore of the particular tribes in the small areas.

These tribes included the Northern Cheyennes, the Dakota Sioux, the Blackfeet, the Crows, in more or less permanent camp circles in the valley of the Missouri and Yellowstone rivers. These groups were of Algonquian ancestry. Tribal legend recorded that many hundreds of "Great Suns" previously they had been driven away from the eastern part of the country, probably by Iroquoian aggression. In their eastern camp circles, they had lived partially by hunting, but also by cultivating the herbal foods. Through the years these food habits persisted. The men were hunters. Women of the tribes took care of the agricultural duties.

There were ritualistic rites to celebrate the first gathering of wild fruits and plants as well as cultivated herbs. They were especially emphasized by tribes of the Northwest Coast, the Plateau region, California, etc. In the areas where agriculture was already dominant or was rapidly becoming so, these rituals were more often associated with maize than they were with all of the other cultivated herbs

98

combined. Legend, folklore, and the earliest crude records tell of Planting rites and ceremonies, Green Corn celebrations, and Harvesting rites. They were especially elaborate in Mexico, Central America, and the Caribbean regions.

For a more intensive study of the similarities and differences of the native Indian population in North America before 1492, the following outline or grouping may be suggested. The arrangement is made according to what might be called "Ecological" or "Environmental" factors, determined by geographical or natural conditions. It will be interesting to note that there is a loose relationship of almost a determinant quality between the physical environment and the cultural and economic development of the people who live and grow in the land which Nature has provided for their use and enjoyment.

Those people who lived in the extreme north—the Eskimos, as we call them—either are of different ancestral stock or their mode of life has differentiated and segregated them from the neighboring tribes, throughout the centuries. This is particularly true east of the Rocky Mountains and Northeastern Canada and Greenland. In the Northwest, Alaska, and the Aleutian Peninsula, there is some evidence of neighborly association. In the entire Arctic region, however, no evidence has been found to indicate that the early people lived otherwise than by fishing, or by hunting sea mammals. If their food occasionally included wild plants, there is no record of it. Anything like agriculture would have been impossible.

Immediately south of the frigid home of the Eskimos,

there is a region characterized by many evergreen forests between which are treeless areas. The early inhabitants of this region, which included part of Alaska and much of Canada, apparently were of the Athapaskan families in the western and west-central territories, and the Algonquian linguistic descendants occupied the regions from Ontario and Quebec to the Atlantic seaboard. Most of their food was the product of hunting and fishing, but there is some evidence of agricultural activities, particularly in Alberta and Saskatchewan. Caribou and moose were abundant and provided much of the food, while the many rivers, lakes, and streams not only furnished an abundance of fish but also gave free access for travel in their birchbark canoes.

Along the Pacific Coast, from the "panhandle" of Alaska, including most of British Columbia, Washington, Oregon, and the extreme northern section of California, there was a distinct difference in the habits and mode of life of the Indian population. Evidences apparently indicate frequent communication with Asiatic tribes, probably by access to an Aleutian bridge. One of the outstanding manifestations of the culture of these early tribes is the totem poles, which seem to set these people apart from the other Indian population. It would not be an exaggeration to say that, in general, their "culture" was greater. Evidently they were not nomadic, but lived in small settlements or villages. They collected stores of material goods and developed social classes, even to the extent of virtual slavery. Ritualism held a high place in their social and religious practices.

Bordering the Coast group, including the plateau of the

Columbia and Frazier rivers, extending from eastern British Columbia, Washington and Oregon, all of Idaho, Alberta, and most of Montana and Wyoming, a cultural group lived, whose history and records show a combination of influences. On the extreme edges, the association with the neighboring tribes is evident. In the center of this area, the Indians were very democratic, showing none of the class consciousness of the Coastal group. They were much more peaceful than the Plains Indians, and their food habits consisted primarily of fish from the Columbia river, the Frazier, and the upper sources of the Missouri and Yellowstone. There is some evidence of beginning cultivation of herbs, used in their rituals and as food. Included in this group were some of the Blackfeet, Crows, Northern Cheyennes, Tetons, and the western fringe of the Sioux.

East of the Plateau region, embracing parts of southern Alberta, eastern Montana and Wyoming, Saskatchewan, Colorado, the Dakotas, Kansas and Nebraska, Oklahoma and Texas, the Great Plains district was the home of the Indians, with whom we are most familiar today.

They were nomadic and lived almost entirely by hunting. Their camp circles were oval in shape, with the opening facing the East, dominated by the large Medicine Lodge. The tribal Medicine Man was more powerful even than the chiefs. Not only was he consulted in matters of health, but his word was law in the ritualistic life of the tribes. While there are no records to show agricultural activities, the use of wild herbs for their mystical and medicinal properties was almost entirely in the hands of

101

the Medicine Man. Their knowledge was amazingly accurate. Belonging in this Culture Group are part of the Cheyennes, most of the Sioux, some tribes of the Blackfeet and Crows, the Comanches, and other groups. Their teepees were of the familiar conical type. After the horse was introduced into America, about 1600, they became expert horsemen. Their semiannual or annual Buffalo hunts, usually carried out in the spring or possibly in the summer, were examples of a religious ritualistic ceremony. Unlike the modern hunters, they did not kill wantonly for sport. Food, shelter, clothing were provided by the herds of bison. Strict rules announced by the Medicine Man governed these tribal hunts.

The states of Wisconsin, Minnesota, Iowa, the eastern parts of the Dakotas, Nebraska and Kansas, all of Arkansas, Missouri, Kentucky and Tennessee, and part of Oklahoma and northern Texas, with all of Illinois and Indiana and Michigan show a distinct difference as compared to the Plains region. The Indian population in this typical prairie country was not nomadic, but tended to have permanent homes in villages that were based on the plan of the camp oval, with the Medicine Lodge facing the East. Agriculture was practiced, with hunting and fishing of minor importance. Their ritualism and celebration of feast days were concerned with gratitude to Great Medicine for bountiful crops of maize. Some of the tribes included in this Culture Group are the Illinois, the Osages, the Pawnees, the Iowas, and the Omahas, among others. The men were the hunters,

102

while most of the agricultural work was taken care of by the women of the tribe in the land adjoining their permanent camp-oval settlements.

Part of Ohio, all of Pennsylvania and New York, and the territory east to the Atlantic and north to the St. Lawrence basin are included in the culture zone where cultivation of maize and other herbs predominated over hunting and fishing. This region also extended southward to embrace all the Southern States and the Gulf Coast as far west as Louisiana.

The State of California south of the Northwest Zone and west of the Sierras exhibits characteristics which differentiate the early Indian population from the surrounding areas. The people inhabiting this area were unique in speech, culture, and physique. In many ways they resembled the tribes much farther south, in Mexico and Central America, although the general picture was entirely different. Around San Francisco Bay and the coast toward the south, Monterey and even as far as San Diego, fishing furnished a large part of their subsistence. In the interior, hunting predominated. Yet both hunting and fishing were merely accessories of convenience and the mainstay of nutrition undoubtedly was furnished by wild plants. The acorn (which of course is not an herb but the seed of a tree) was dried, ground into meal, and leached with water. The seeds of several wild herbs were similarly treated. The productivity of California soil and the mild winters prevented famine. Gathering the wild plants and their seeds

103

was probably the work of the women, either alone or with the other women. Girls were taught the significance of this work and the rituals that always accompanied it.

The Indian girls were taught the folklore about plants—that they were a direct outpouring of the love of the Great Spirit for His children; that they were placed on earth to be used as food and for healing; that if they were used rightly the rain spirits would bless the land. These sayings were exemplified in the ceremony at the time of the first gathering of the herbs. The Indian girls who gathered these first products were not allowed to eat any of their first materials that were taken. They were prepared, dried, or otherwise treated by the women, and stored in the community house or teepee.

The plant products to which this rite applied varied with the tribe and surroundings. It was berries in the North and Northwest; berries and roots in the Plateau region; mostly seeds in California and the Great Basin.

An elaborate ritual marked the "First Plant Food" of the season in a majority of the tribes, especially on the Northwest Coast, in the Plateau district, in California, in the oasis in Mexico, in Central America, on the prairies, and in the East. While it varied to some extent in the different localities and tribes, in the main it conformed to a well-defined pattern.

When any crop was approximately half-ripe, the Chief —or in many instances the shamans, or medicine men— would call on the people to begin their harvest. The Indians would then assemble in answer to the summons, with the exposed parts of their bodies painted with a red stain. The shaman stood before them, holding a birchbark dish or tray filled with fruit, berries, or whatever crop was about to ripen, or perhaps a collection of all products. Raising the tray on high, he addressed the spirits of the mountain, or the rain spirits, or successively the four winds—north, east, west, and south—in the following manner: "Oh, Great Medicine (or whatever name applied to the particular spirit) we tell you we are going to eat this food. Give us plenty that we may prosper." Then the shaman went around the circle of tribesmen, according to the path of the sun in the sky, and gave each of them one piece of the food from the tray. After that, all the women went into the fields and gathered berries, or fruit, or herbs, or whatever the crop was. The appeal was to the spirits of the natural forces to assure a good crop. Similar rites were held for fish, for hunting, and for the harvesting of maize. In many tribes there was a sacred ceremony to the rain god or rain spirit, in addition to the "First-Fruits" ritual. The specific form and wording varied, of course, with the individual tribes and different environments, but the underlying motivation must be interpreted as identical throughout the centuries, from the earliest Paleo-Indian groups to modern times. Some form of Supreme being, or energy, or power is present in every manifestation of nature.

In the territory east of the Sierras, extending to the Plains district, researchers have found evidences of more cultivation of food plants and medicinal herbs than at any other of the northwestern areas. The climate was to an

105

extent semiarid; wild plants did not grow so profusely; fishing was less bountiful; and hunting was not entirely satisfactory. This region was just beyond the western boundary of the great bison herds of the plains. Maize probably was the most important cultivated crop, and the various rituals and ceremonies were adapted to its planting, harvesting, grinding, and storage.

The early inhabitants of New Mexico, southern Arizona, northern Mexico, and Baja California constituted another quite distinct area of cultural development. Rainfall in this area was problematical. Fishing was limited mostly to the Rio Grande and the lower Colorado. Hunting was good, occasionally, in the mountains and high plateaus, but not of sufficient quantity to provide subsistence.

The people were gregarious—that is, they lived together in permanent villages. The cliff dwellings and pueblos of the Southwest are existing artifacts that tell of the culture of these early people. Their food habits were largely cultivated herbs and herbal products, predominantly maize, supplemented by occasional products of hunting. Rituals connected with all ceremonies were sometimes weird, but always significant. Each pueblo had its own organization, its own customs, and its individual existence. Since culture can be described as a combination of all the practices in the daily life of a group, the culture of the cliff dwellers and Pueblo Indians bridges the gap between the Stone Age and the Metallic. A study of the ritualism and folklore of these tribes is fascinating, and it furnishes a basis for a

106

better understanding of the importance of plants as food and for healing purposes.

In the ancient days, the people who lived in these cliff houses and pueblos, far above the surrounding plateaus, had to climb to their homes by stone ladders or steps hewn out of the rock walls. The fields where their maize or herbs were cultivated were far below, on the flat lands. These crops were maize, beans, squashes, and melons, and after the rituals of harvest the products had to be carried up the steep trail and rock ladders to the community storehouse on the mesa pueblo above. There, community life was largely dominated by sachems.

Continuing southward through Mexico, we come to the Aztec and Mayan culture areas as distinguished from the Zunis farther north. It is intensely fascinating to study the development of all these people, especially the Mayan economy. Also, it is one of the strong arguments advanced by the proponents of the Atlantis-Lemuria land-bridge theory to account for the advanced culture which the early Spanish explorers found.

From the foregoing comments regarding the habits of the Indian population it seems evident that the climate and geographical surroundings had much influence on the developing culture and sustenance of the people.

In addition to the environmental factor, hereditary tendencies must be considered. As a general conclusion, it should be realized that soil conditions and rainfall determined the development of agricultural activities; that culti-

107

vated herbs were increasingly used in the eastern coastal regions, in the area bordering the Gulf of Mexico, and in the Pacific valleys and plateaus. It seems quite evident that there is a gradual increase in the cultural aspect of the ritualism and in the recognition of the healing properties of herbs and herbal products as we journey from north to south. As has been indicated, the cause may be explained partially by the hereditary factors and customs of the various tribes, but also the environmental and geographical influences must be taken into consideration.

Except in the far North, Northwest, extreme Northeast, and the Great Plains district, where hunting and fishing predominated, indisputable evidence has been discovered by archaeologists and researchers that, before the arrival of the white man in 1492, cultivated herbs such as maize, beans, squash, pumpkins, gourds, and other vegetables were part of the daily food habits of the early Indians.

CHAPTER EIGHT

Indian Herbal Rituals

LEGEND AND HISTORY BLEND IN THE ALMOST fabulous stories about the magical effectiveness and healing properties of the Indian herb mixtures, teas, and poultices, and their medicinal and marvelous healing effects. In all the tribes, the ritualistic ceremonies and tribal welfare were the direct responsibility of the medicine man and his assistants. In most instances, he had more real power than the chiefs.

From an extensive study of Indian folklore, legends, and history of the various tribes that inhabited North America, plus many visits to Indian Reservations and conversations with both the old men and the younger ones, a general conclusion can be reached. While the practices and customs, both ancient and modern, varied to a certain extent because of hereditary and environmental differences, a basic pattern is evident that appears to permeate the lives of both Paleo-Indians and their descendants. This pattern can be expressed by considering two related factors.

First, regardless of their origin or subsequent habitation in North America, the Indians were fundamentally "mystical minded." That is, they loved ritualistic portrayal of their beliefs, customs, and ceremonies. All the tribes had many celebrations, some religious and some commonplace, from simple rites to those lasting for several days. However, every ritual was based on a recognition of the great power and universality of Great Medicine, or The Great Spirit, although naturally the different tribes had individual names for their Supreme Being and the lesser spirits who demonstrated that power.

The second factor was that in all the ceremonies various herbs and herbal products were used to demonstrate the emotion depicted by the particular event being celebrated. The properties of the herbs used were related to the effect desired.

Before the white men came and ruined the idealistic and beautiful philosophy of the Indians in the name of "progress," the term "The Noble Red Man" was more than a mere phrase. Studies conducted by The American Museum of Natural History, Smithsonian Institution, the United States Department of Agriculture, and individual archaeologists and ethnologists have brought life to ancient legends and folklore of the early inhabitants of North America.

Consideration of these reports leads inevitably to the natural conclusion that there is a common ground underlying them—a similarity in origin. The variations from tribe to tribe can be explained by the realization that climatic and environmental influences have accounted for the differences in the details of the stories related by the old men of the tribes around the campfires at night. The primary fact that permeates all the stories is that the Supreme Deity, Great Spirit, Great Medicine, God, or whatever name they assigned to Him, was an all-powerful Ruler and that this power always manifested through Nature—through growing plants, and because animals ate the plants all living beings could partake of this power. Many examples illustrate this fact.

In all the tribes where maize was cultivated, there were several ritualistic ceremonies, including the feast at planting time, the appearance of the first ears, the beginning of the harvest, and the storage of the grain for future sustenance. The shaman, or medicine man (who was called "Sachem" in some tribes), presided over these occasions, some of which lasted for several days. Probably the most elaborate rituals were those practiced by the Algonquins and the Iroquois in the East and Northeast.

There were three powerful Indian nations in the East and Northeast. The most populous was the Algonquian, but they were not so well organized as the Iroquois federation —five tribes: The Oneidas, Mohawks, Senecas, Onondagas, and Cayugas. This association apparently was based on a blood relationship. Among themselves, in their home life, they were peaceful. Their villages were permanent, each "lodge" had its own plot of land, where the women of the tribe raised the maize and beans and squash and pumpkins and gourds and other herbs which constituted the bulk of their food. It was a communal life. When the early French missionaries came to the new land, shortly after A.D. 1600, they found this closely knit village life, where the women

111

were the dominant providers. The long-houses were the property of the women, who were the builders and the agricultural workers. The men were allowed to live with them as long as they behaved themselves. The crops of maize and other herbs and tobacco were community property, stored in especially built long-houses for that purpose. Their houses were from fifty to one hundred feet long, built of poles and covered with bark.

The interior was divided by partitions, open to a central area or passageway. These cubicles were anywhere from eight to twenty feet in size, all connecting and open on the center area. At each end was a door, covered with bark. The men of the tribe were soldiers and hunters, and they were very warlike where the neighboring tribes were concerned. The people relished an occasional ration of meat to supplement their herb diet. At certain intervals along the central passageway there were pits dug, for fire, with openings in the roof above for smoke to escape. It was like a community of four family apartments. If there were four fire pits, for example, that long-house would accommodate sixteen families. At an early age, the young girls were instructed by their mothers in the mystical lore of the herbs used for food and incense, about the techniques used in gathering or harvesting the different crops, their storage in the community house, and above all the care of the growing plants and their preparation for food and for incense. There was a special ceremony at the planting time, another at the gathering of the first crop, still others as the growth proceeded.

Because of varying geographical and climatic conditions, these celebrations partook of the nature of the main crop harvested. In the East and Northeast, among the Iroquois, the Hurons and the Algonquins, and their related neighbors, maize was the primary cultivated herb. Others were beans, lentils, gourds, pumpkins, squash, and various others.

The Indians of the Northwest Coast especially venerated the first crop of berries, whether cultivated or wild. Berries or roots were revered in the Plateau regions. Seeds were gathered in California, also in the Great Basin. In the Oasis country to the south, and in Mexico and Central America, the principal crop was corn, with seeds a close second, and herbs of the gourd family almost as important.

The "First-Fruits" ritual was practiced by most of the tribes, with variations to accord with the particular crop. An example of this ceremony, from the stories, folklore, and observation of the tribes living on what is known as the Plateau, including parts of Montana, Wyoming, the Dakotas, Colorado, southern Alberta, and Saskatchewan, is given. The tribes in this region included the Mandan, or Dakota Sioux, the Northern Cheyennes, the Crow, Arapaho, Gros Ventres, Assiniboin, and certain of the Pawnees. One of the main crops consisted of native wild and cultivated herbal fruits and berries.

When the crop was approximately half ripe, the medicine man, or shaman, would call on the members of the tribe to begin picking the fruit. The people all assembled before the chief and the shaman, with the exposed parts of

113

their bodies painted red. The medicine man and his trusted helpers went to each member of the group, holding bark trays on which were piled individual fruits or berries, offering each Indian a berry. After all had been served, the shaman raised the container on high, facing the East, then the North, the West, and the South, then back to the East again, meanwhile chanting a prayer: "Oh, Great Medicine, All Powerful One, we thank you for all growing plants that give food. We appeal to the spirits of the hills and mountains to give us a good berry crop."

If the ceremony was to celebrate the first fruits of some other product of Nature, then the name of that plant would be substituted for "berry." The same general type of appeal, with proper variations, was used for the harvest time and the storage procedure. The first fruit rites were closely related to the first game rites, the fish rites, and the wild and cultivated seed ceremonies in the various tribes.

After all had partaken of the offering, the shaman announced, "Now let everybody go out and gather berries!" (Or fruit, or other herb food.) Whereupon, all the women of the tribe went to the fields to harvest the products that were ripe. It would all be placed in the common storehouse, for future use. The women were free to eat as much as they wanted to while they were picking the fruit, with one exception. The young girls who were participating in the ceremony for the first time were not allowed to eat during their "initiation," but were free to do so thereafter.

In some tribes, incense was burned during the celebration. It might have been called a religious feast.

114

The Nez Percés in Idaho, the Blackfeet, Gros Ventres, Assiniboins, Northern Cheyennes, and Crows in Montana, all had similar ritualistic ceremonies, all related to the herbs and herbal products that meant life sustenance to them. Farther south, the Shoshones and Utes in Utah, the Arapaho, Western Sioux, and Southern Cheyennes in Wyoming and Colorado, and the Arikara and Mandan Sioux in the western Dakota country were very devout in their celebrations of the many appeals to Great Medicine for bountiful harvests and abundant food.

In the plains region to the East, some of the tribes had semipermanent camp circles, where growing plants, either wild or cultivated, were used for food. Many of these, however, were nomadic, and they followed the movements of the buffalo herds, which were their chief means of preserving life. Their use of herbs was confined to wild growth, which furnished some food and also material for incense and medicinal purposes.

Taking the Northern Cheyennes as an example, it will be of interest to note an intimate view of their home life. They were quite warlike where other neighboring tribes were concerned, but their intra-tribal attitude was peaceful in the extreme. During the day, the men of the tribe and camp circle were busy, either as warriors or hunters or in other various ways. The women were either weaving, making garments, tanning hides, or busy with the wild and cultivated herbs.

They had no written language, and of course no literature. Every communication was by word of mouth. The

115

medicine men usually acted as "soul doctors" during the evenings, after the day's work was done. The people would gather around the fire, usually built in the center of the camp oval, behind the medicine lodge. It was like a big family party. Anyone was free to talk, and the shaman usually acted as master of ceremonies. Their entertainment during these evenings consisted principally of speechmaking, general friendly conversation, and storytelling. One of the old men of the tribe or the shaman himself was usually the storyteller. The most popular types of stories had to do with the tribal folklore, tales of legendary tribal heroes and ancient tribal customs. Many of them depicted miraculous powers of healing or other marvelous results from the use of herbs and herbal products. Many tribes exhibited themes in their tales that were so similar in type that it indicated a probable common origin in the culture pattern of the different groups. One of the most interesting was related to the author by a very old Cheyenne warrior, a survivor of the famous Custer Battle, during the celebration of the fiftieth anniversary of the Battle of the Little Big Horn, in Hardin, Montana, in 1926. The same legend, with variations, is in the folklore of other tribes in addition to the Cheyennes.

SEES IN THE NIGHT

Many great suns ago, when the world was young and the Great Spirit or Great Medicine took pleasure in His Chosen People, the Cheyennes, a man-child was born to a Shaman Chief, Bold Eagle, and his wife, Singing Fawn. The young

116

brave grew strong and excelled in all the mysteries of the people, but he was lonely, because he had few friends among the other boys. Then Bold Eagle and Singing Fawn were killed by a raiding party of the Crow tribe, and Jumping Rabbit was left alone. He mourned for them but tried to continue his efforts to do some worthy deed so he could earn his warrior name. As a child, he had been given the name, Jumping Rabbit, because of his activity. But he wanted a braver-sounding name. He must earn it. He offered herbs to Great Medicine, endured the herbal ceremonies in the sweat lodge and the four day's herbal sacrifice in the Lodge of Great Medicine. But still it did not come.

The camp circle was moving toward a river. All the people were hungry because it had been a dry time, without rain, and the crops of herbs had not done so well. They came to the river and the rest of the people crossed. Jumping Rabbit was tired, so he sat down under a bush and went to sleep. He dreamed that a mother dog with four puppies had been left behind when the people had crossed the river. She was howling and singing a song in dog language. He awoke to find that it was true.

The mother dog was approaching him, singing a song. Then she howled four times like a wolf and spoke to him in a language which he could understand. "Jumping Rabbit, do not harm my babies," she said. Then she sang a different song, and howled four times again like a wolf.

"I will help you, Mother," Jumping Rabbit answered. He carried the puppies across the river and then helped her across. The people in the camp circle had gone ahead, and were no longer in sight. When all were safe, the dog spoke, after singing another different song and howling four times. "Wū hǔ ǐs tǎt′ tǎn," she said, which in the ancient Algonquian language means, "I am a human being." Then she told him that she had power of magic; that because he had helped her, she would help him. "What is it that you most desire?" she asked.

"To do some brave act that will win for me my warrior name. Jumping Rabbit is childish, and I have reached the number of great suns that tell me I am no longer a child. I have given many gifts of herbs to Great Medicine. Can you help me?"

"Yes, I will help you. The people of the camp circle have gone on ahead. We can reach them by travelling at night. In four days they will go on a war trail. Do not go with them, but wait two suns. Then go at night. Take another young man with you, but do not tell him about me. I will be with you, but you will not be able to see me."

It all happened just as the mother dog said. When they reached the main body of Indians, just as the sun, the representative of Great Medicine, began his travel across the sky, they found that the young men were preparing for a raid against a party of Crows in a nearby camp oval. The shaman, whose name was Ho′-Im′-A-Ha, (which means "Winter-Man") was burning many herbs and chanting a ritual to the Spirit who rules success. Some of the people asked Jumping Rabbit to join them, but he said, "No. I will wait one sleep and two suns. Then I will go." He remem-

118

bered the instructions of the mother dog. He selected as his companion another young man, intelligent and brave. Jumping Rabbit told this friend, Gray Wolf, something about his plans, but he did not mention the mother dog.

After two suns, they started. There was no moon, and it was very dark. However, Jumping had no difficulty in following the trail. The rising sun greeted them on the second morning. They faced the East, and made an offering of herbs to Great Medicine. That day, because of their presence, they took the Crow camp by surprise, and made off with many horses. That happened four times. At the end of the fourth successful day, Jumping Rabbit heard, as in a dream, the voice of the mother dog, speaking in the ancient Algonquian language. He looked around, but could not see her.

"Kiutu gim-a mipena" and again, "Kiutu gim-a mipena," which means, "You will be a chief!"

Then he saw her, but he sensed that he was the only one to behold this vision. Instead of a dog, a beautiful Indian maiden was smiling at him, reaching her hand to him, beckoning him to her. She sang the familiar songs, her voice sounding like the lovely ripple of a mountain stream as it flows over white pebbles. At the end, she howled four times like a wolf. Then she spoke again: "The Great Spirit is much pleased with you. Because you showed compassion to the mother dog, and because you have obeyed all desires I have told to you, your reward will be great. When you travel at night, you will be able to see as if it were day. We will return to our home camp circle, and you will be honored by a ritual with herbal offerings, and will receive your warrior name, 'Sees-In-The-Night.'

"I am blessed with magic powers, and this ability to see and understand is given to you. You shall marry me and our children will possess this gift which always passes from mother to daughter. My human name is $Ē$ $hyōph$ $stâ$ which means 'Yellow hair' and wherever I am I bring success and plenty." It all came to pass as she said. Sees-In-The-Night became a great chief and he and Yellow Hair lived for many great suns and had many sons and daughters. Wherever they went they brought success and happiness.

There are many stories in the folklore of various tribes that in some respects seem to show a common origin. That might indicate that throughout the entire Indian population of the Americas, particularly of North America, there existed a hereditary line of tradition and belief that permeated their ritualistic existence. Some phase of this would influence and manifest the religious or semireligious activities, with regional variations due to different environmental factors.

Close study and painstaking research regarding the Indian culture and life habits reveals unmistakably that fact that their fundamental belief in the supernatural was indissolubly linked with intense religious fervor. Their Great Spirit was all powerful and omnipresent. He delegated control of the activities of life to lesser spirits who must be placated or cajoled or praised in order to bring success to any undertaking.

That applied to making war, hunting, fishing, and the

120

daily activities in agriculture, raising crops of herbs for food, gathering the harvest, preparation of the stored grain or other foods, and all of their habits of life. This was particularly true in their search for food, which of course was fundamental in their existence.

Plants and animals were all personified in the Indian belief. In hunting, the animals were considered to be as much responsible for their capture as were the actual means of taking them. The spirits that controlled the animals must be placated before the hunt, to bring success. At the time of the annual buffalo hunt, for example, there usually was a two-day ritual, directed to the spirit of the hunt, with votive offerings of herbs and definite ceremonies under the direction of the shaman, assisted by the leading chief and the underchiefs. In these demonstrations the authority of the medicine man was paramount. He organized and directed the activities. The principle involved was that the animals must be placated by their spirits in order that they might be taken!

The rituals for successful farming and gathering of crops did not depend on pleasing the crops, but the Rain-Making ceremony was important to persuade the spirit governing growing plants to bring an abundant crop of maize or other food product. Always it featured herbal offerings of appropriate nature. The spirit who caused rain must be pleased before the gift could be received. Certain herbs and herbal products were considered to be sacred. For example, peyote was especially prized, since its hallucinations reinforced and increased the religious convictions of the user.

121

While the shaman was in many ways the social and, to a certain extent, the political director of tribal activities, his chief function in all cases was the healing of disease. The sickness could be either physical or mental. Whatever the cause, the appropriate spirit must be appeased or pleased, and the usual method was with offerings of proper herbs or herbal products. The dominance of the religious influence in the treatment of disease by the medicine men was natural, because he was the spiritual director of all tribal activities. In most instances, his position enabled him to control the political and warlike tendencies as well. Sanction of all the actions of the people was supposed to rest with the Supreme Being, Great Medicine, The Great Spirit, or whatever name they gave to the Supernatural Ruler. The Medicine Man's attunement to this Being naturally gave him the ability to render valuable help.

Among the various tribes, it was thought that all diseases were caused by the displeasure of one or more of the spirits that controlled either a long list of animals or even natural phenomena such as thunder, lightning, drought, meteorological events, reptiles, birds, or insects. Each spirit was responsible for a particular disease. To give relief from the symptoms of the spirit's displeasure, offerings were made, which often consisted of various herbal concoctions, either given to the patient internally, or as a poultice, or burned as a sacrifice to the spirit.

In different parts of the country, the wild growth of herbs varied to a certain extent, but in general, it has been discovered that certain families of herbs apparently are native, either in genera or species, regardless of location. It is interesting to realize that most of the tribes used similar combinations of herbs in their treatment of disease. Poultices, applications of the leaves, stems, or roots, mixing the herb combination with food or drink, and offering the herbs to the spirit or spirits by burning were some of the methods of treatment used.

Researches indicate that more than fifty different species or varieties of herbs were used by Indian Medicine Men, in various combinations, for the treatment of diseases. The majority of ailments and diseases were thought to be of supernatural origin and because of that, they could be cured or treated only by the supernatural, with ritual, herbal offerings, and through the intervention of the shaman.

Most shamans used tobacco, either to contact their spirit helpers or to banish disease from the body of the patient. The native tobacco was used in many, if not most of the religious rituals, regardless of the nature of the ceremony. It was sometimes smoked, often chewed or snuffed. And its most widespread use was burning it as incense. Smoking the medicine pipe was a sacred part of tribal celebrations, whether political, war-preparation or for healing purposes.

The use of alcoholic beverages was closely connected to the healing activities of the shamans, as well as to the food habits of the people. Two notable examples, particularly in the Southwest and Mexico and Central America are maguey (*Agave*) and Dasylirion. Wine was made from them, which we know today as pulque. In addition, they were among the staple foods used by the people. Several other plants, including maize, from which beer and wine were made by some tribes, fermented honey by the Mayans, the wine palm, from which a potent wine was made in Central America and by the Aztecs, and wild plums, pineapples, and sarsaparilla root furnished alcoholic beverages. The use of herbs for this purpose was less common in the East and Southeast than it was in the Southwest and Mexico and Central America, where it was usually associated with religious ceremonies, also with other sacred rituals, and in healing. Certain herbs were the source of narcotics, which were used as medicines and as charms to bring rain and perform other miracles by the shamans.

Some of the herbs used by the tribes for healing purposes included many that are the source of valuable remedies that are familiar today. In a pamphlet published by the United States Department of Agriculture, listing some of the herbs that were prized by Indians and early pioneers, are references to plants that are well known, either as wild life or cultivated in gardens.

The plant known as Alumroot (*Heuchera spp*) has rootstalks that show astringent properties. It was used by the early Indians and also by the pioneer settlers to relieve the symptoms of diarrhea.

It has been reported that some species or varieties of the common Aster were greatly prized by the Hopi Indians and other tribes for their medicinal properties, possibly as a part of their incense rituals.

Birds and small animals relish the fruit of the Bearberry

Honeysuckle. The Indians of Alaska and British Columbia are said to have eaten the fruit of this herb, both fresh and dried. Some of the varieties of this plant, whose botanical name is *Lonicera involuncrata,* are reputed to cause vomiting, or have a laxative effect.

Specific reports have come that the Navajo and Hopi Indians used the flowers and fruit of Bull Thistle (*Cirsium drummondia*) for its medicinal qualities for various disorders.

The tender leaves and stems of the common Cowparsnip (*Heraclium lanatum*) were considered a delicacy as food among several tribes, particularly in the Southwest. The powdered roots were used for healing purposes, notably for rubbing on the gums when teeth were loose, as a solution in water to apply on the body to reduce fever, and as a relief for rheumatism.

The seeds of the many members of the mustard family (*Cruciferae*) furnished oil of mustard which was used medicinally to stimulate the skin. The green leaves of some species were then, as now, eaten as greens. Botanically related plants such as cabbage, cauliflower, kale, and radishes were cultivated to be used as food, also.

The roots of Elkweed (*Swertia speciosa*) were powdered and mixed with warm water and applied by the early Indians as a lotion to reduce fever. That remedy is still in use by some of the tribes in Southern California. It has been found that large doses taken internally can prove fatal. In small quantities it appears to be an effective laxative. Another use, reported by Indian authorities, was to

125

grind the roots coarsely and mix them with lard. This was rubbed on the head to kill lice. Reputedly, these roots were eaten as food by the Apaches.

Several species of Geranium (*Geranium spp*) have medicinal properties, notably to slow down profuse bleeding. This was practiced by tribes in Southwest America.

Early Spanish settlers in New Mexico learned from the Indians to use the flowers and leaves of Indian Paintbrush (*Castilleja spp*) to treat kidney ailments. The Zuni Indians also prized this herb for the black dye it produced, to color deerskins. They also used its medicinal properties for skin disorders.

While the common tall Larkspur (*Delphinium spp*) apparently is deadly to cattle, and less so to horses and sheep, the Indians used to grind it and mix it with corn meal to give the corn a blue color. This flowering herb gets its common name because the blossoms are shaped like the spur of the bird. The flowers and leaves were used in mixtures of plants for incense purposes.

The plants of the Mint family (*Labiatae*) were and are widely distributed, and the pleasing aroma from its leaves was enjoyed by the Indians, both in incense and as flavoring for foods. For example, the Hopi Indians used it in the early days for flavoring the mush made from ground maize. That practice still persists in modern tribes.

Ligusticum porteri, an herb whose common name is OSHA, is related to Celery, and has a somewhat similar slightly pungent odor. Its leaves were useful to flavor stews and soups. In addition, the Apache Indians smoked the

126

dried stems, and this practice was adopted by the early Spanish settlers.

One variety of Pentstemon was used by Navajo Indians and early settlers in New Mexico as a treatment for kidney troubles. They also boiled the flowers to make a remedy for whooping cough. The Zuni Indians are said to have rubbed this syrup on their arrows and "rabbit sticks" during the preliminary ritual before a hunt. It was thought that this would give success to the hunt.

Skyrocket Gilia (*Gilia aggregata*) was a favorite remedy of the Navajos. The dried leaves were used to treat stomach ailments. The Hopi Indians ground the flowers with their maize to make an offering to the spirits of the hunt before setting out in pursuit of antelope.

The herbs belonging to the Spurge family (Genus *Euphorbia*) were thought by the Indians to be efficacious in treating snake bite. The Pima Indians used the ground root to cause vomiting.

Useful garden varieties of herbs in the Parsley family (*Umbelliferae*) include parsnips, celery, carrots, etc., which were raised for food by the Indians.

The Zuni Indians maintained that the leaves of the common Western Yarrow (*Achillea lanulosa*) were cooling if they were applied to the skin. They chewed the flowers and roots and rubbed the pulp on the bodies of the shaman and others who were working in ceremonies that used fire as part of the ritual. This herb was thought to be potent as a love charm.

CHAPTER NINE

The Earliest Agriculturists

THERE IS A GRADUAL TRANSITION IN TYPE AND manner of life among the Indian inhabitants in what may be called the Middle Americas. From the Cliff Dwellers of the Southwestern States, through the Aztecs of Mexico, including the various "mystery" people of Central America and the Maya civilization and the hidden tribes of Yucatan, there is an amazing record of genuine, permanent community life, which was not new, but apparently a continuation of centuries-old racial behavior.

Archaeologists and ethnologists are by no means in complete agreement regarding the quite advanced culture that was evident among the Indian population in Central and South America when the earliest explorers came. Artifacts from the excavations prove beyond reasonable doubt that these settlements were made at least 11,000 or 12,000 years ago, as demonstrated by the carbon 14 test. Further, from caves in Mexico and Central America, unmistakable vegetable remains have been discovered that, by the carbon 14 test, are definitely of the same age. These are not the remains of wild plants, but cultivated herbs, indicating an

129

agricultural mode of life of these Paleo-Indians. It is reasonable, then, to think of the ancestors of the Aztecs, Mayans, Incas of South America and other related tribes as the first farmers in the world.

According to investigations by the National Geographic Society, a study of the South American prehistoric civilization has proved this to be true. It is reasonable to assume that cultivated herbs and herbal products constituted a large part of the subsistence of the Indian population prior to the coming of Columbus and the French and Spanish explorers.

Climatic conditions and other geographical factors undoubtedly offer a partial explanation of the increase in agricultural activity among the early tribes in New Mexico, Arizona, Southern California, Mexico, and Central America, but that reasoning does not fully account for the almost definite line of demarcation that is so evident. There is and was a radical difference in the characteristics and habits of the Indians inhabiting California north of present-day Los Angeles, Nevada, Colorado, Utah, from western Texas north and east, and the tribes in New Mexico, Arizona, southern California and southward through Mexico. This was evident not only in the increase in agriculture, but also in family life, tribal organization, religion, and linguistic stock. Consideration of these factors leads to the natural conclusion that the ancestry of these two groups was different.

It has been proved that Middle America and South America were inhabited at least ten to twelve thousand years ago and it is equally certain that a form of agriculture was practiced in the very early days. The earliest Spanish explorers, shortly after A.D. 1500 discovered well-organized farming operations, where the people lived in communal settlements, villages, or cities, surrounded by fields where herbs were grown for food. Hunting was a comparatively minor activity because game was scarce. The few rivers offered little opportunity for fishing, except in the coastal areas. The growing of crops was naturally dependent on rainfall, so the ritualistic ceremonies emphasized appeals to the god or spirit that controlled the weather. The shamans or medicine men were rainmakers as well as healers and in some instances magicians.

In many tribes the training of a shaman was a matter of rigid discipline. He was usually selected at an early age and became a neophyte or apprentice after studying and working with the chief shaman for one great sun. It usually required three great suns' intensive training until he was proclaimed an expert medicine man.

From the cliff-dwelling, Pueblo tribes living in Colorado southward, to the unique complications of the Aztec and Mayan life in Mexico and Central America, observation gives definite evidence of an increasing dependence on agriculture as a primary means of sustaining life. A typical example is the pueblos of the Mesa Verde Indians, who once flourished in Colorado, Arizona, and New Mexico, and southward into Old Mexico. The most noteworthy is the cave village in Mesa Verde National Park, Colorado. This was a ruined relic when Coronado explored the region

131

early in the 1500's. It was forgotten until about 1888, when it was "rediscovered" by some cowboys. The archaeological researches have revealed that these Cliff Dwellers were undoubtedly the earliest agriculturists, who built their almost impregnable pueblo homes, sometimes four, six, or even eight tiers high, as a protection against nomadic, warlike tribes. Large fields for cultivation of their herbal foods surrounded the pueblos. Researchers have discovered that maize (or corn) was undoubtedly the principal crop, although beans, gourds, and many other herbs were grown. An outgrowth of their agricultural activities was basketmaking. The materials used were the fibers of plants, canes, and stems. The artistry of the Indian basketry is well known today. Among the early Pueblo Indians, alcohol and alcoholic drinks were banned. The principal drink was *atole,* which was made from corn.

The people must have understood at least the rudiments of engineering, because irrigation canals, constructed thousands of years ago, brought the waters of the Gila and other rivers to the agricultural lands of Arizona and New Mexico. Some of these have been restored for use today.

The most noteworthy of all tribes that practiced this irrigation engineering were the early Hohokam people. The National Geographic Society researchers have reported an archaeological discovery of one ruined city nine miles from the nearest river, whose waters flowed through an irrigation canal seven feet deep and approximately thirty feet wide at the top. It has been estimated that these prehistoric canals brought water for agricultural use for a total of more than two hundred thousand acres.

In the Pueblo country, the early Indians considered that their land was the center of all creation. The phenomena of Nature were all explained by the shamans in terms of religious rituals, especially designed to please the particular spirit or deity that caused or controlled the demonstration. These lengthy ceremonies had deep significance to the Indians, particularly those which had to do with his daily life and his sustenance. They conceived a genuine affection for The Corn Mother, the Maiden Spirits who were associated with other herbs, such as squash, lentils, beans, turnips, carrots, and others, the deity who brought rain that the crops might grow and mature, and all other spirits who could make their lives happy and prosperous.

There were elaborate ceremonies at planting time, before the harvest, and at every important event that concerned the welfare of the tribal members. Among the most spectacular of the rituals was the Snake Dance of the Hopi Indians. Carried out under the direction of the shaman, it lasted for many days. Each tribe had "Warrior Societies" that were semisecret. Two of these, among the Hopi group, were the Antelopes and the Snake Society. Four days before the ritual began, members of the Snake organization would leave the camp circle or village, two by two, in the quest for snakes. The first day they searched the north country. On the second they went west; the third day they covered the south, while on the fourth the "snake gathering" was completed in the sacred East, the land of the rising sun—the representative of the Great Spirit. Most of the snakes collected were rattlesnakes, which were placed in a special basket, a large container in the "kiva" or lodge room.

The fifth, sixth, and seventh days were devoted to ritualistic prayers and dances inside the kivas, with offerings of herbs, to the deity of rain. During the eighth day the first ceremonial dances were held outside the lodge rooms. Chants and prayers to the rain-gods featured this ritual, along with herbal offerings.

The most spectacular feature of the ritual began early on the ninth day. The snakes were brought from the kivas. The Antelope priests, followed by the priests of the Snake Society, then came from their kivas and danced solemnly around, stamping vigorously with foot drums. That was to let the gods of the underworld know that the ceremony had started. The circuit was completed four times. They then faced each other, chanting under the leadership of the shaman.

Working in groups of three, the Snake Priests marched with dignity to the snake pit, where the first priest would pick up a snake and grasp it firmly between his teeth, holding it about the middle of the reptile's body, so that the snake's head would have more freedom of movement. With the snake in his mouth, he danced down the length of the large assembly room, while the second priest danced beside him, using a whip or wand tipped with feathers or herb fibers to distract the snake's attention. At the end of the march, the snake was dropped, when it was picked up by the third priest. When the priest dancer dropped his snake, he immediately returned to the snake pit for another, and repeated the performance. After all the snakes had been danced with, the chief of the snake priests sprinkled corn meal along the lines of a large circle that was divided into six parts, four of which represented North, South, West, and East. The other two were dedicated to the zenith, where the above-gods had their abode, and the nadir, reputed to be the home of the ground spirits. Then the snakes were all brought out and cast into this circle. Now, the women of the tribe brought more corn meal and sprinkled it on the serpents.

After another chant to bless the corn crops, the priests all made a rush to the circle, where they picked up as many snakes as they could manage in both hands and holding their squirming, wriggling burdens at arms' length, they ran out of the room and down the ladders or steps from the pueblo to the flat fields below, where they released the reptiles to the North, South, West and East. Their belief was that the snakes would carry the news of the successful ritual to the rain-gods. Among the modern Indians today it is legendary that often rain came, sometimes in a cloudburst!

Even in these days of complicated living, the rain priests of certain tribes still chant their mystical rituals; the dancers, wearing hideous masks, continue the solemn obligation to placate the above spirits and the below spirits that control the needed rain. When the clouds are opened and

135

the blessed moisture comes to insure a bountiful crop, their sublime faith manifests in another ritual of thanksgiving. The Indians of ancient times and those of today who have not been spoiled by white men's cupidity believe fervently that their gods, with unlimited power, are still able to control the destiny of living, from north to south, from west to east, in the happy hunting grounds above, and in the warm earth beneath. Times change, and men change with them, but certain fundamental beliefs and habits of thought apparently are ingrained in all human consciousness.

The word CULTURE has been interpreted in many ways by various people throughout the ages. Its meaning has been influenced by ethnological development, by environmental factors, by moral standards as well as economic opportunities. The average person today probably will consider culture as more or less synonymous with scientific achievement. A relatively small minority possibly will maintain that it should be judged by intellectual attainment only. In applying any or all of these criteria to a particular section of the human race, it must be realized that

> All the world's a stage,
> And all the men and women merely
> players.
> They have their exits and their en-
> trances;
> And one man in his time plays many
> parts, . . .

Consider the question of morality, for example. In many early tribes, it was considered highly moral to kill and eat other beings. Human sacrifices were not only sanctioned but commanded by religious belief and practice. History is replete with examples of tortures and what we consider unethical acts in the name of religion. Yet among many tribes where practices such as these were a part of daily existence, archaeological researchers have brought to light the proved fact that a high culture had developed, even before the dawn of history. That was particularly true with the Aztecs and related tribes in southern Mexico, the Maya group in Yucatan and Central America, the Panamanian people, and the Inca civilization in Peru and neighboring states in South America.

Archaeological findings have proved beyond the shadow of a doubt that the basic occupation of these Indians was agriculture. Maize (corn) was undoubtedly the principal crop, with several varieties of beans, lentils, gourds, parsnips, tomatoes, and other vegetables and herbs. It has been stated by historians and proved by archaeological findings that when the Aztecs came, early in the fourteenth century, they found a high degree of civilization already existing among the inhabitants, supposedly the tribe known as Acolhuacans who lived near a large lake. Tradition relates that the Aztecs were mainly hunters at that time, but that they acquired their culture from the people already there. For several decades they lived peacefully, it is related, but about the year 1370 the Acolhuacans drove them away from their land. Then the chief shaman of the Aztecs had a dream, as legend reports it, that they would be led to another beautiful lake, with an island in its center. They would see an eagle, sitting on a cactus plant, eating a serpent. That would be the signal to tell them where to establish their homes. That legend is commemorated in the design of the Mexican flag.

History and research depict the Aztec nation and their neighbors as cruel, bloodthirsty warriors. Their religious fanaticism centered around hideous, despotic gods that delighted in human sacrificial offerings, in addition to the votary gifts of herbs and herbal products. Yet they, along with their predecessors and the other tribes of the middle Americas were the world's earliest farmers on a large scale. The cultivation of the herbs for food and ritualistic purposes was almost entirely work for the women of the cities and communities.

Both men and women were active in the artistic construction that beautified their homes and cities. Traditional beliefs were portrayed in buildings and sculptures. All events in life were themes for the ritualistic memorials engineered by their shamans. Herbs were even used in the gruesome ceremonies accompanying human sacrifices. Many varieties of herbs and ground fruits were grown and elaborate concoctions were made for the daily sustenance of the families. On the lakes and waterways floating islands on rafts often were seen, where vegetables were grown.

The Aztecs worshipped corn gods and goddesses. Stealing corn was punishable by death, or at least by slavery.

Tortillas made from corn meal have changed very little since the early days, except that evidence from artifacts indicates that tortillas in pre-Columbian days were larger than those of the present time.

In addition to the bloodthirsty human sacrifice rites, the ancient Aztecs and the Toltecs before them had a great many ritualistic celebrations, and the main offerings in these ceremonies were flowers, fruit, and herbs. Social dancing was a favorite pastime of these people, and there also decorations and offerings of flowers and other herbal products were common practice.

The mystery of the Maya of Yucatan has intrigued historians and archaeologists for many years. The complete solution of their origin is still hidden. It is common knowledge today that the Maya originated and produced one of the first calendars—perhaps the first in the Western world—which, with their system of chronology, is even more accurate than our Gregorian calendar. It is not so well known, however, that the astronomical and meteorological calculations undoubtedly came into being because the Maya people were agriculturists! More than that; they practiced scientific farming. Undoubtedly the main crop was corn, or maize.

It was in 1921 that archaeologists discovered a large statue in Guatemala, which represents the God of the Harvest, sowing grains of corn on the Earth Mother, which wears a headdress of the "feathered serpent." It has been estimated that the ritualistic practices and accurate scientific, astronomical and mathematical achievements of these people began many thousands of years ago. The calculated

139

dates of their origin parallel the earliest suppositions regarding the culture of ancient Egypt and Mesopotamia.

Because the Maya people were primarily farmers, naturally they were not only interested in the various seasons of the year as that affected the growing of crops, but their very livelihood depended on climatic conditions. It is conjectured that the efficient calendar was a direct result of that necessity. It is not too much to say, then, that herbalism—the study of growing plants and their life-giving value—had a far-reaching effect in the development of Mayan culture.

Because of their scientific handling of the business of agriculture and the recognition of the seasons, they developed a better and more efficient use of time. That provided more leisure time, and they were able to give more attention to architecture, sculpture, and other fine arts. Many public buildings, temples, and grand structures were built of stone and decorated with stucco and paintings, when pretentious cities grew in the early days of the Mayan empire. The priests were adepts in astronomy as well as students of the ancient mysteries and their close study of the weather probabilities and meteorological influences resulted in more abundant harvests and stored food reserves.

Another close parallel to the culture of ancient Egypt and Mesopotamia is evidenced by the many pyramids and temples. These pyramids were the ziggurats, or stepped structures similar to the earliest pyramid in Egypt—that erected by Imhotep during the reign of Zoser—except the

Mayan ones are usually not wholly of stone, but principally just faced with it.

The youths and maidens in the Maya confederation were surrounded by mystical concepts, astronomical and astrological applications, all leading to deep religious fervor. Every event had its own meaning and its own patron god or spirit. Underlying all of it was the raising of herbs for food.

The magnificent cities, the temples and pyramids which they built were not the homes of the common people, but were dedicated and sanctified to the ceremonial rituals and priestly activities. The nobility and the priests lived in homes built in the outskirts of the great ceremonial structures. The people had their homes in closely surrounding villages. However, all members of the community had free access to the mysteries of the temples and observatories, where the priests plied their esoteric rites with sacrificial offerings to the spirits and deities that would give abundant food and happy weather conditions to supply that food.

The pre-Columbian Indian life in Panama furnishes a link to explain the amazing similarities that existed between the Maya and Aztec groups in Mexico and Yucatan, and the Incas of South America. From all researches it is tentatively thought that the culture of the tribes in Panama derives more of its characteristics from the Inca civilization than from the Maya group. No record has been found of human sacrifices either among the Panamanian Paleo-Indi-

141

ans or the Incas or their predecessors. Yet many of the customs of this early civilization are so similar to those of the Mexican and Central American culture that a comparison is interesting. The use of herbs, particularly corn as their main source of foods, definitely places them in the agricultural field of occupations.

Archaeologists have discovered that the predecessors of the Inca civilization in the Andean region of South America were the Chimu people, who built large cities, surrounded by irrigated, terraced farm lands. The walls of these terraces are still standing, and they are mute tribute to the great culture of these prehistoric people. There is a rumor, as yet not proved to be true, that the ancestors of these pre-Inca Paleo-Indians came from the East; that they were tall, light-haired, and highly developed mentally with a culture that surpassed even modern standards. That rumor or folklore has been linked to the many tales relating to the origin and history of the inhabitants of Easter Island.

The Incas probably appeared in the Andean highlands about A.D. 1000 to 1200. Their history before that time is problematical and still unveiled. It is thought that they probably were a relatively small tribe, living in the Andean highlands, but that a racial instinct impelled them to migrate to the lower country around what is now Cuzco; to take over the ruined remains of their predecessors, and to expand and develop a remarkably efficient cultural civilization. According to legend and reports of the early Spanish explorers, the Inca people were sun-worshippers. This does not mean that the sun itself was their god, but it was the visible representative of the spiritual deity who was all-powerful.*

That brings up another theory that has been advanced regarding their origin. The legend most commonly accredited to the Inca themselves is that a leader of the tribe, Manco Capac, had a vision, prophetic in nature. He believed the revelation that many great suns previously their people had lived and ruled in the lower lands, and that they were destined to rebuild their former empire. Accordingly, he and his sister-wife, Mama Ocllo, led the tribe to the fertile valley, where they gained domination by peaceful and mystical demonstration. A tall young man named Roca, of the nobility, was arrayed in a robe covered with gold spangles, and he stood in the mouth of a cave, where the sun was reflected with dazzling brightness. The awe-stricken multitudes assumed that he was a Son of the Sun, come to earth to rule the people. The young man took the name of Sinchi Roca, (meaning War Chief Roca). He was the first really historical ruler.

The farmlands of the Incas were models of scientific agriculture. Some were on the flatlands surrounding the villages and cities, while those on the hillsides were expertly terraced, with walls of masonry or stone. All were adequately supplied with water from perfectly engineered irrigation canals, many of which survive at the present time. While corn (maize) was the principal crop and the

* (This is similar to Pharaoh Akhnaton's adoration of Aton, symbol of the sole god.)

mainstay of their food, in the beginning of their empire development, at least, it was not long before other herbal crops began to take great prominence.

Various species of beans, gourds, leafy vegetables, and condiments were of increasing importance in their agricultural activities. One fact is probably not generally known. Inca Land was the original home of our common white potato. However, it was known and grown many hundred years before the development of the great Inca empire. Legend, history, and research show that the predecessors of the Incas discovered that the small tubers of the potato plant were good to eat. As farmers, they nourished it and developed varieties which would grow at different altitudes, from sea level up to 14,000 feet. When the Incas came, they developed it further by their scientific farming, until it became a major crop.

When the Spanish conquistadores arrived, they were after gold, and paid little attention to such a lowly thing as herbal crops. Some of the adventurers took potatoes home when they returned to Spain, where they remained almost unnoticed for many years. Eventually some were taken to Ireland, and thence to New England, where they were given the common name Irish Potatoes. Today, of course, the potato is one of the staple food crops, particularly in America. We might say, "Potatoes were born in Peru and grew to adulthood in North America."

The marvelous system of roads which the Incas built to bring their crops to markets would do credit to modern engineering practice. There were paved superhighways, provided with steps on the hillsides, and suspension bridges where the roads crossed a chasm. Although wheels were unknown, transportation was by foot or, in the case of the high nobility, by litter carried by humans, who were honored to be selected for that purpose. The herbs and herbal products were loaded on llamas and the central markets were picturesque examples of a happy people whose governing representatives promoted harmony and peace, as befitted the beneficent Ruler of All Being, the Divine Inca, the Sun God, whose representative on Earth was the Sun.

There were no money problems. Every transaction was by barter. With their agricultural activities raised to a high degree of perfection, scientifically administered, they had the urge and the time to devote their attention to architectural procedures. Their massive structures, great temples, public buildings, and stepped pyramids are similar to those of ancient Egypt. They had no machines and no tools except the inclined plane, the crowbar and stone and bronze or copper knives. Great stones were transported over long distances by concentrated man power. Polishing the rocks which weighed many tons was by patient grinding with sand and water.

Historically, the Inca Emperor who brought the realm to its highest development, was Pachacutec, who ruled from about 1400–1448. He reasoned that there is a God much higher than the Sun, that this supreme God, Viracocha, was the Creator of all; and was all-powerful. One of his sayings is preserved by Spanish historians: "The physician herbalist who is ignorant of the virtues of herbs, or who, knowing the use of some, has not attained to all knowledge, knows little. He should work until he knows all, both useful as well as injurious plants, in order to preserve the name to which he pretends."

PART THREE

THE AMERICAN HERITAGE

CHAPTER TEN

Herbs Are Health Builders

ALTHOUGH MANY PEOPLE DO NOT REALIZE IT, in our busy modern life we are dependent on herbs and herbal products in almost every activity. If our minds are affected by negative thoughts, our objective senses tell us that we are indisposed, ailing, or sick, and we immediately summon a physician or go to the drug store. Most of the medicines prescribed or purchased owe their healing or pain-relieving value to the properties of the herbs or herbal products which they contain. Many sleep-producing drugs affect the nervous system or the circulation or both, due to the presence of morphine, opium, or one of its derivatives.

Opium is the active principle of the opium poppy, *Papaver somniferum*. This herb was known in ancient Egypt, Palestine, Carthage, Phoenicia, Greece, and Rome. It also was grown by the monks in many of the medieval monasteries for its medicinal properties. It is fascinating to trace the history of the growth and uses of this herb, which has had such a fantastically combined beneficial and deleterious effect on human welfare throughout history. In ancient times among the Greeks, the poppy was considered a love charm, while the Romans revered it as symbolizing peaceful, restful sleep.

The modern curse of the drug habit is too well known to merit lengthy discussion. It illustrates, however, that some herbal products, if not rightly used, can become harmful as well as beneficial to man.

Another species of poppy, *Papaver rhoeas,* has been cultivated for its delightful seeds, which have been described as "walnut flavored." This species probably was developed in the Dutch Province of Zeeland.

Several varieties of *Papaver rhoeas* include both annual and perennial herbs which can be grown from seed. In more temperate or warmer climates the plants will grow to a larger size or greater height. The green stems and leaves, often faintly tinged with a delicate bluish sheen, contrast pleasingly with the flowers, which in many varieties are white, with an iridescence like the interior of a shell. However, in the California poppy the four-leafed petals are yellow. In some Oriental plants, the flowers may be more brilliantly colored.

The seed pod of the poppy is cut as soon as it turns brown, but it must not be so dry that it will break open and scatter the seeds. If the poppies are raised in the home garden, the pods are further dried on a cloth sheet or screen, in a shady, dry location. The very small, globular seeds can be rubbed out of the dried pods and more completely dried, and they are ready for use. Everyone is familiar with the poppy-seed decorations on cookies, cakes, and other pastries. The addition of poppy seeds to other dishes, such as fruit, vegetables, salads, and so forth, gives a nutlike flavor.

The seeds of some of the more inferior varieties are compressed to make poppy oil, which is used by artists in oil painting, and as a substitute for the more expensive olive oil. Poppy seeds are also an ingredient in many bird-seed mixtures.

"A ROSE IS A ROSE IS A ROSE IS A ROSE—"

Throughout history, in fact and fiction, in literature, music and the arts, rhapsodies have been written about the rose as a symbol of esoteric charm and mystical beauty. It is almost synonymous with mysticism. Through the ages, it has brought both tragedy and joy, war and peace, love and hate.

Because the stems of many roses often contain woody fiber, they cannot be classed botanically as herbs. But in legend, literature, folklore, and romance, since time immemorial, the ROSE has been the Queen of Herbs, the inspiration of poets, symbol of light, life and love, health and beauty, with a secret, mystical connotation. Can we let a technical, botanical point prevent consideration of the beneficial influence of roses on human welfare? Perfect physical health begins with an untroubled mind; beauty and health are inseparable.

Most modern roses are hybrids from three original species. The DAMASK ROSE (*Rosa damascena*) was brought to Europe from Damascus during the Crusades. The CHINA ROSE (*Rosa chinensis*) originated in China. The

151

exotic ROSE de PROVINS (*Rosa gallica*) is a native of France. To trace the story of the development of all the varieties we have today would require a library of volumes.

Shakespeare expressed it beautifully in his TRIBUTE TO A ROSE:

> O, how much more doth beauty beauteous seem
> By that sweet ornament which truth doth give!
> The rose looks fair, but fairer we it deem
> For that sweet odor which doth in it live.
> The canker-blooms have full as deep a dye
> As the perfumed tincture of the roses,
> Hang on such thorns and play as wantonly
> When summer's breath their masked buds discloses:
> But, for their virtue only is their show,
> They live unwoo'd and unrespected fade,
> Die to themselves. Sweet roses do not so;
> Of their sweet deaths are sweetest odors made:
> And so of you, beauteous and lovely youth,
> When thou shalt fade, my verse distills your truth.

There are many herbs that can be grown in the home garden, which will add beauty to the surroundings as well as to provide food for health. Whether one grows these plants for the pleasure of having "an old-fashioned garden" or for their utilitarian and superior gastronomic properties —in other words, to use as food—it must be realized that all living entities are dual in nature. Each is composed of a positive quantity plus a negative unit.

In plants, the pollen is the positive part and the ovum is the negative. Almost all of our flowering plants, including the majority of herbs, are monoecious—that is, they have the stamens, bearing the pollen, and the pistil and ovary with the egg or ovum on the same flower. If one plant has only staminate flowers, and another plant of the same species bears only pistillate blossoms, that variety is said to be dioecious—that is, male and female plants are individual.

The increasing complexity in the development of physiological division of labor, from the simplest amoeba-like forms of life, through the vegetable kingdom and the animal kingdom, up to man, is a fascinating study in evolution.

A seed is a fertilized ovum. All of the plants we consider as herbs grow from seeds. Since "Nothing can not give rise to something," the seed must contain all the elements for growth into the mature plant. Yet such is the inconsistency of the average person today that we customarily discard all seeds in most fruits and berries and vegetables because we think the seeds are not beneficial to health. There are food macerators and blenders on the market today, which will give us the benefit of the health-giving seeds as well as the fruit or berries or pulp or leaves or roots of the herbs themselves. Oftentimes the greatest benefit of an herb lies in its seeds.

Near Escondido, California, there is a large ranch which among other things promotes herbs as health builders. The Health Ranch is owned and operated by Dr. Bernard Jensen, who also is the author of books and pamphlets relative to the use of herbs as food.

Grateful acknowledgment is due to Doctor Jensen for

153

SEEDS AS FOOD
The Nutritive Wealth of 100 Grams of Seeds

Seed	Protein (%)	Carbohydrate (%)	Fat (%)	Linoleic Acid (g)	Thiamin (mg)	Riboflavin (mg)	Niacin (mg)
Beans, Navy	7.8	21.2	0.6	trace	0.14	0.07	0.7
Beans, mung	24.2	60.3	1.3	—*	0.38	0.21	2.6
Cowpeas	9.0	21.8	0.8	—*	0.43	0.13	1.6
Lentils	24.7	60.1	1.1	—*	0.37	0.22	2.0
Oatmeal	14.2	68.2	7.4	2	0.60	0.14	1.0
Peanuts	26.0	18.6	47.5	14	1.14	0.13	17.2
Peas, raw	6.3	14.4	0.4	—*	0.35	0.14	2.9
Rice polish	12.1	57.7	12.8	—*	1.84	0.18	28.2
Rye wafer	13.0	76.3	1.2	—*	0.32	0.25	1.2
Safflower seed kernels	19.1	12.4	59.5	43	1.12	0.40	2.2
Sesame seeds	18.6	21.6	49.1	21	0.98	0.24	5.4
Soybeans	34.1	33.5	17.7	3	1.10	0.31	2.2
Sunflower seeds	24.0	19.9	47.3	30	1.96	0.23	5.4
Wheat germ	26.6	46.7	10.9	5	2.01	0.68	4.2

* These amounts have not yet been determined.

much of the following material, which is taken from his book, SEEDS AND SPROUTS FOR LIFE.

A spore, a seed, or an egg—by whatever name we may call it—is the "being" from which all living things develop; therefore, the seed must contain all the necessary potentials for developing, continuing existence—for life itself. In Genesis 1:29, we read, "And God said, Behold, I have given you every herb bearing seed, which *is* upon the face of all the earth, and every tree, in the which *is* the fruit of a tree yielding seed; to you it shall be for meat." The word "meat" of course means food.

Seeds are the procreators of life. Seeds contain the highest percentage of protein of all the foods in the vegetable kingdom and they also have nearly all of the ten essential amino acids. We may say that seeds represent the secret of life. In the tombs of the ancient Egyptian Pharaohs, more than three thousand years old, seeds have been found, which when planted, have grown. All the life-giving elements are found in seeds and they are there for our good. Many physicians and dieticians have recommended the use of seeds as food, because of their high mineral, vitamin, and protein content.

Seeds are especially rich in Vitamin B Complex and in Vitamin E, which is the heart, nerve, and reproduction vitamin. It has been called the "antisterility" factor. It is most important for happy human existence. Both Vitamin B and Vitamin E are consistently discarded in modern milling and refining of foods.

Most seeds are excellent sources for Vitamin F, which is

classified an "Unsaturated Fatty Acid." But little cooking is recommended for fats and oils, because a high temperature renders fats indigestible and Vitamin F is destroyed. Other delicate vitamins are easily destroyed by prolonged cooking, so we should try to eat as many raw vegetables as possible, for health's sake.

Probably the most familiar uses of seeds as food are the common breakfast cereals, the most important of which, from a nutritional standpoint are corn, wheat, rye, oats, barley, millet, and brown rice. The use of these cereal grains in human diet antedates history. Legend and history blend in their reports of the food habits of primitive man, through the developing civilization of tribes and nations, up to the so-called refinement and progress of modern practices. The grains—the seeds of herbs—have been one of the staples in food consumption. Let's compare a scene in our great-great-grandparents' life with a similar incident in the modern rush and bustle, trying to keep up with the neighbors.

Great-great-grandma wants to bake some corn bread. She calls to her husband, who is dozing on the parlor sofa, or watching a fly that is trying to find an opening in the window. "Hiram! Will you get me some corn, please?"

"I will, Martha." He uncoils his long legs, gets up, stretches, and goes through the back door to the corn crib, where he selects several ears of beautifully ripened yellow corn. He carries them back to the woodshed, puts them into a stone mortar, and pounds them to a coarse meal with another stone. Great-great-grandma is pleased. She says, "Thank you, darling," and proceeds to bake delicious corn bread, one of Hiram's favorites, to be eaten with pure clover honey. Ummmm!

Today, Alicia, Martha's great-great-granddaughter is studying a recently published cook book. One recipe catches her eye. "Hmmm! That sounds good," she comments. Search of well-filled shelves fails to reveal the ingredient she wants. She goes to the living room. Arthur, her husband, is watching television. It's the seventh inning. The Giants are leading the Dodgers 7 to 5. "Art, dear," she says, sweetly, "I'm trying a wonderful new recipe and I haven't any corn meal. Will you go to the store and get some?"

"Oh, I suppose so. Can't you wait till this game's over?"

"The store might be closed," Alicia objected.

Art left, grumbling. The new and exceptionally obliging clerk lowered his voice. "The only corn meal we have is bleached, with chemical preservative added. If you want pure corn meal, there's a Health-Food store two blocks up the street. They are higher priced, but—"

"I'm in a hurry," Art said. "I'll take this."

The game was just ending when he reached home. The Giants won, 9–8. The label on the package read:

"SUPERIOR CORN MEAL"
Nature's Product
Chemical Preservative Added

Foodwise, there is much to be said and thought about The Good Old Days. Each step in the streamlined proces-

157

sion toward energy-saving convenience has degenerated the food values of our life-giving herbs and seeds.

Cereals should be cooked with as little heat as possible. It has been suggested that in cooking rice, wheat, or other grains, one half cup (or one cup) of the cereal be placed in a one pint (or one quart) thermos and covered with boiling water. Let it stand for four of five hours or overnight. The cereal will be cooked. The addition of raisins, butter, or soy milk will give a very tasty dish.

The factor of variety in our food habits should not be overlooked, for obvious reasons. If we consider wheat and corn and possibly oats as cereals and forget that rye, millet, brown rice, barley, and other seed grains are also very valuable additions to our daily rations, we are overlooking an important fact in nutrition. Changing weather conditions, individual daily energy output, temperature variations, and so forth, demand a health program based on individual needs, not only in the matter of cereal grains, but also in our general food program. Truly, "Variety is the spice of life" in regard to foods as well as in other activities.

There are some food producers and milling companies who have their material analyzed for exact mineral content. One can now buy brands of flour and cereals that are guaranteed to be rich in the natural composition of minerals, because they have been grown by organic gardening in the naturally rich soil, without the addition of artificial chemical fertilizers or poisonous insecticides. By using such grains, cereals, and flour, we get all the elements that God intended us to have. Do they cost more? Yes, they do, but they are worth it, from the standpoint of health.

Barley was a staple food, even before recorded history. In the Old Testament in Biblical times, incidents are related to "the barley harvest" and in Greece, particularly in Sparta, barley was a standard food for building strong bodies. It is high in protein, carbohydrates, and minerals. A source of heat and energy as well as a tissue builder and vitalizer, barley soup is especially appetizing. When mixed with other vegetables (grains or seeds) it adds a flavor that is delicious and unforgettable. In addition to its value as a soup ingredient, barley steamed in a double boiler makes an excellent breakfast cereal, with honey and fresh fruit and cream (or soy milk). Barley flour is useful in baking. Muffins made with barley delight one's taste. Barley is particularly beneficial if one is troubled with digestive weakness, as it is easier to digest than other cereals, particularly oats. It is non-gas-forming. Folklore tells its use as a remedy to prevent the spread of infections. The "Pearled" barley one buys in the stores is the original product of Nature, with the outer skin and many of the vitamins removed, to "make it look better." The unpearled grain is much superior. It is an all-purpose food, particularly beneficial to nerves and muscles, and furnishes heat and energy, and is a ready source of important vitamins. It is effective in keeping the joints of the body supple.

Another cereal grain that is extremely beneficial in nutrition is BUCKWHEAT. Many doctors recommend it because it contains rutin, which is a flavenoid that

159

strengthens the walls of the arteries, tends to reduce blood pressure and relieves varicose veins. In addition to rutin, buckwheat is very rich in Vitamin B-Complex and Vitamin E, which has been proved to be the "reproductive" vitamin, and also Vitamin C. The use of rutin is invaluable in cases of stroke caused by rupture of small veins in the head and buckwheat may help to prevent this condition because of its rutin content. It is much better to include in our diet the foods that will give us these necessary and valuable additions than to pay good money for a lot of concentrates and artificial food supplements. The natural, unrefined buckwheat may be dark in color, but commercial "processing" removes much of the vitamin value and the natural grain is much to be preferred. It may be used as a cereal, or buckwheat flour made into muffins or pancakes or bread.

CORN is especially valuable because of its high magnesium content. Magnesium is needed in the diet because it promotes bowel activity, is a natural laxative, and raises the "tone" of the intestinal tract. If yellow corn-on-the-cob can be eaten raw, it is one of the most perfect nutrients. Boiling will destroy some of the valuable vitamins—roasting is not so harmful. But for full value, the raw, juicy succulence is best. Many American Indian tribes used yellow corn as one of their main foods, and their healthy bodies and stamina are traditional. Corn oil is beneficial to the entire body. If the raw corn can be crushed and made into a soup, and the hulls strained out, it makes a dish suitable for people even on a restricted diet. The hulls are

160

the only part that may cause irritation. Yellow corn meal mush is excellent, as are corn bread, muffins, etc.

DILL SEED and ANISE SEED: These are frequently confused, because in the Bible Dill seed is often referred to as Anise. They are of different botanical families. The Dill belongs to the Parsley group. The Anise, *Pimpinella anismus,* is a native of Southern Europe and Northern Africa. The genus of the Dill is *Anethum*. Both plants yield seeds that are highly esteemed as food flavors.

Most of the foods which we classify as cereals are the seeds of herbs. In addition to the common ones that we accept without thinking about it, there are three which deserve more than a passing mention.

Practically everyone has heard of MILLET, (*Panicum millaceum*) but few realize that it is top quality in nourishment when its seeds are used as a cereal grain. It is cultivated in the United States largely as a forage crop for stock. In Europe it is used extensively as a cereal. In ancient times, in Egypt and the Mediterranean lands, it was a staple item in human diet. As early as 500 B.C., Pythagoras recommended Millet for inclusion in the diet of his fellow vegetarians. According to archaeological records, it formed part of the food of prehistoric man. In India, forty million acres are given over to its cultivation and production.

The following was taken largely from Dr. Bernard Jensen's book, for which grateful acknowledgment is given:

The high food value of Millet has been recognized in America by such eminent researchers as Doctor Kellogg of

161

Battle Creek Sanitarium and Doctors Osborn and Mendel of Yale University. Their studies show that it is a complete food, being high in protein (with a good balance of amino acids) rich in minerals (calcium high) and vitamins, especially riboflavin, one of the most important vitamins in the B-Group, and also the very essential lecithin. One cup (8 ounces) of uncooked millet contains 22.6 grams of protein. It is an alkaline-forming food that is easily digestible. It is especially valuable in wheat-free and allergy diets.

Doctor Jensen concludes his discussion of MILLET with the statement: "Use millet in all seasons. It is the best seed cereal you can eat. It is one of the best protein grain foods and will not put fat on the body. It is an excellent extender for meat loaves, being such a good quality protein."

Another herb which until recently has been neglected as a source of excellent food, is the SESAME plant and seed. It is a native of the East Indies. The dictionary gives the information: "Sesame—An East Indian herb, (*Sesamium indicum*), bearing seeds which are used as food and as the source of the pale yellow oil, Sesame Oil, used as an emollient." The dictionary description gives only a small part of the story.

Sesame plants are now grown successfully and quite abundantly in China, Africa, India, Central America, South America, and in the southwestern part of the United States. It is an annual herb, growing to a height of about two feet. It is quite sturdy. The seed, which has been called the queen of oil-bearing seeds, is very stable; it can be stored for long periods of time and it resists oxidative rancidity. It is 45% protein and 55% oil. Nine pounds of seeds will give two quarts of oil.

"Tahini" is liquefied Sesame seeds. It has been estimated that two tablespoonfuls of Tahini contain protein equivalent to that in a sixteen-ounce steak. It is high in lecithin and unsaturated fatty acids, minerals, phosphorus, niacin, and Vitamin E for the heart, blood vessels, and oxygen utilization. It is high in the amino acid, methionine.

The dictionary, under the heading CHIA, says that the herb, CHIA, is a Californian and Mexican herb (*Salvia columbariae*) belonging to the Mint family, whose seeds yield a pleasant beverage and an oil, Chia Oil. That, however, is only part of the story. Legend and early history relate that centuries ago, in ancient India, a tiny blackish seed, a member of the mint family, was recognized as a great energizer. That has been its function during the passing years, in many lands.

Today, health-conscious individuals are recognizing that it furnishes excellent nourishment. A sturdy winter annual, it grows to a height of twenty inches to two feet, and the common name for this herb is "Thistle Sage." It blossoms during the winter, from November until March or April. The leaves tend to have a purplish color, along with the green, and the flowers are blue.

The benefits of chia seed as an addition to food can hardly be overestimated. Many have reported great results. Some have even said that it is a second "elixir of life." One seventy-year-old "hard rock" miner attributed his great energy to the fact that he adds one teaspoonful of chia seed to his lone meal of "flapjacks." A young married couple reported, "We have more pep!" One physician wrote, "Chia seeds are exceedingly nutritious and are readily borne by the stomach, even when that organ refuses to tolerate other food." In the old days, the Mission Fathers valued Chia Tea for lowering fevers—and they used the seed as a poultice after shotgun wounds!

CHAPTER ELEVEN

Nature Knows Best

IN THESE DAYS OF MODERN SCIENCE, ELEC-
tronics, synthetic chemistry, and nuclear physics, industries and educators apparently have joined forces in an
endeavor that seems to have many laudable aspects. Our
public education systems, from the grades through high
school, college, and university, are being increasingly
geared to assist the big industries in developing a race of
superscientists. Millions of dollars spent by the giant manufacturing establishments for research and advertising
have resulted in a veritable flood of synthetic products,
notably foods, that lend themselves to spectacular advertising and meet a largely artificial public demand for novelty,
eye appeal or labor saving.

Of course the advertising for these prepared foods will
stress the health-building and nutritional properties of
their products, and the labels on packaged or canned foods
will state that they conform to the requirements of the
Federal Food and Drug Law, but, usually in finer print, at
the bottom of the label is a statement that "So and So"
(almost always given just as initials) "has been added as a

preservative." While most of these additives are harmless in small quantities, some of them may have a cumulative effect in the human mechanism. This might seriously interfere with the enzyme or hormone action of the human digestive process. Nature's food nourishes the body. Artificial, synthetic food materials, no matter how well they are advertised or how beautifully they are packaged, can not have the nutritional value of Nature's own products.

Chemical vitamins are usually added to the processed foods, in a laudable endeavor to increase their value. It is logical to assume, however, that these chemical vitamins do not have the vitality of Nature's own growth.

The question may be asked, "Is it possible to get all the nourishment one needs, for health, by eating only organically grown foods—herbs, berries, fruit, or animal products —without the chemical additives which scientific research has provided?" The answer is an emphatic, "YES!"

According to an old definition, "Science is an orderly, systematic pursuit of knowledge." The word "pursuit" of course implies that complete knowledge is always ahead of the pursuer. It is the lure of the chase, the joy and satisfaction of new discoveries that characterize the true scientist. The individual who claims to know everything about any subject is just "kidding" himself, but nobody else.

A true story is told about a college class in chemistry. One day some students asked a question, in all seriousness. The professor looked over his glasses, grinned, and said, "I don't know the answer to that." Then he went on, "When I was taking my postgraduate work in Germany, the head of the department, 'the old man' as we called him, went away for a few days and left the class in charge of a young quizmaster who thought he knew everything. We students wanted some fun, so we asked him some technical questions. He answered, using many technical words, but his explanation didn't mean anything. We thanked him. When 'the old man' returned, we asked him the same questions. He said, 'Huh! Nobody knows that!'. The moral, of course is, If you don't know a certain thing, don't be ashamed to admit it. If you should know it, get busy and find out. If it's inconsequential, it makes no difference whether you know it or not."

The study of pure, organically grown foods and their effect in nutrition is truly a science—an orderly, systematic pursuit of knowledge. We begin with the fundamental fact, Nature never makes a mistake. That is true because Nature always operates according to immutable laws of the Universe, not man-made additions or so-called improvements of those laws. When we gain additional information regarding the manifestations of Nature's chemistry and/or alchemy as they affect human welfare, we are building the structure of Truth, step by step, in our pursuit of knowledge.

Foods are classified according to their chemical content and their function in human physiology. Carbohydrates include sugars and starches, which may be called the framework of energy and the link between plant growth and animal structure. Proteins are those foods which furnish the essential element, nitrogen, in a form which is

167

available for human metabolism. Fats and oils are usually complex in their chemical composition. They serve to augment certain features in the total assimilative process and to furnish specific values of their own in the laboratory of the body. Mineral salts are necessary in bone building, hormone and enzyme composition and in the addition of certain chemical elements necessary for metabolism. Water is the universal solvent, and in combination with other constituents builds up the bulk of human tissues. To these five, the vitamin content of foods has been of increasing importance in the study of physiological chemistry. Nature has provided all of these requirements in the organically grown herbs and herbal products.

One biological distinction between plants and animals is that in the vegetable world, plants have the power to manufacture their own food from Nature's raw materials, air, and water. Animals are dependent on plants for the preparation of their food materials.

The term, photosynthesis, is familiar to the majority of people in today's world of scientific knowledge. It refers to the process by which green plants manufacture their own food—starch and plant sugars. The essential substance is the green coloring matter of plants, which is Chlorophyll. This may be called the "Chief Engineer" that controls the chemical process by which water drawn up from the soil combines with carbon dioxide from the air to produce starch. From this beginning, by further chemical processes within the plant body, we have cellulose, which is the ingredient of plant fibers, and the various plant sugars—

dextrose, fructose, levulose, and others, all of which are "built" by the photosynthetic process. Cellulose is not only a basic ingredient of plant fibers; it is also an essential part of the cell walls of all animals, including man—*Homo sapiens.*

The starches and sugars are not the only things plants have to offer as food, however. Because water is known as the universal solvent, the moisture which is drawn up through the roots by capillarity and osmosis contains dissolved mineral elements which are stored and utilized by the chemical laboratory of the growing plant, along with the starches and plant sugars. A study of growing plants, particularly herbs, will convince the student that all the constituents of complete food and healthful nutrition are to be found in Nature's laboratory.

Ecology is the study of plants and animals as they influence and are influenced by their environment. For example, some soils are deficient in certain chemical elements necessary for complete nutrition. The answer to that, of course, is fertilization. However, there are two kinds of fertilizers. Organic fertilizers are Nature's own answer. Chemical, synthetic fertilizers are manufactured to sell, and often are deleterious instead of beneficial.

If the soil water is contaminated from any source, the plants of course can't reason. They obey the fundamental laws of capillarity and osmosis. The consequence is that the poisonous substances are absorbed and become a part of the plant. Serious illness or even death has resulted from eating fruit, berries, greens, or other products which have been treated with insecticides. Washing the food is not enough. It merely removes part of the surface contamination. The soil water, however, is absorbed in the cells of the plant itself, and washing cannot remove that. Organic gardening is the safe answer to this ever-growing problem. "Better be safe than sorry!"

It should not be forgotten that the common cereal grains are the seeds of herbs. When the word "cereal" is mentioned, the majority of people think first of the various wheat products on the market, and the highly advertised "Breakfast Foods." There are, however, many other cereal grains, the seeds of herbs, that should be considered.

Scientific farming takes into consideration the rotation of crops. Why not apply the same principle to our nutritive problems? Varying climatic conditions, different energy demands in daily occupations, and a host of other factors ought to be considered in planning our nutriment program. The old saying, "Variety is the spice of life" is true with reference to foods as well as to other aspects of life. In our modern times, the average person has become so pampered by "processed" or "prepared" foods that he might find it difficult to adapt his eating habits to conform to the olden days, when people ate for nourishment rather than because certain foods are highly recommended by advertising or sales campaigns. Due to the operations known as "processing," grains pass through many hands before they reach our kitchens. Each process removes some beneficial food value.

We may define life as the manifestation of Nature's laws from the embryo through the adult being, whether it be plant or animal. The seeds of plants contain all the essential factors that will produce and continue the life of that particular unit. When a fertilized seed is planted in good soil, with available moisture, it germinates—that is, it begins its active existence as a growing manifestation of Nature. In the germination process, Life Forces take charge, and definite chemical changes occur, as the tender growth seeks the life-giving sunlight.

Most noteworthy of these changes is the appearance of the green coloring matter, chlorophyll, the engineer of the life-building process. The partnership between chlorophyll and the vital life force from the sun will produce the miracle of complete nutritive value in the growing plant, God's gift to man. When the tiny shoots appear above the ground, we say that the seed has sprouted. These sprouts contain all the vital ingredients of the seeds, plus the chemical changes that have rearranged those elements to give us vitamins, hormones, and enzymes as well as the basic food constituents. Nature is truly bountiful.

It is possible to sprout all seeds. However, some are easier or more satisfactory than others. Alfalfa seeds are probably the easiest and best. The alfalfa sprouts are the highest source of Vitamin C. Also the element Silicon is present, and this is important in nutrition, as it is apparently necessary for nerve communication from the brain to the muscular structure of the body. In plants it controls the ease and rapidity of root to fruit coordination. Vitamin C takes care of germ life, and builds resistance to colds and catarrhal discharges. All sprouted seeds ere excellent for

171

this purpose. Not only alfalfa, but all the legumes, such as peas, any of the varieties of beans, lentils, etc., and the common cereals, corn, wheat, rye, oats, barley, millet, etc., can be sprouted with profit.

All herbs develop from seeds. When seeds germinate, they begin to sprout. These early "sprouts" are at their highest succulence soon after the two tiny leaves make their appearance, approximately four to seven days from the time they start above the soil surface. At that stage of growth, all sprouts have the same general appearance, but as the leaves begin to develop, each species of herb will furnish its own particular flavor.

Sprouts may be eaten raw, chopped and added to green salads, or as a garnishment for other foods; in casserole dishes, omelets, salad dressings, or in sandwiches or fruit juices. Various sprouts can be added to almost any vegetable and they will give a delicate addition to both flavor and nutrition. They may also be steamed and served with a flavorful herb dressing for a most delicious novelty.

In recent years, The National Medical-Physical Research Foundation, of Boston, Massachusetts, has been conducting a series of investigations on the effect of herb sprouts on the possible harmful radiations from television screens. One of their researchers, Ann Wigmore, has developed quite startling results, using sprouted wheat. As reported by Dr. Bernard Jensen in his book, SEEDS AND SPROUTS FOR LIFE, the wheat sprouts, and presumably others as well, can absorb and neutralize these rays or radiations, making them lose their effect on the body.

172

These results lead to the natural conclusion that harmful radiations can be taken up and neutralized by green, growing plant life. Undoubtedly the beneficial effect is due to the chlorophyll of the green plants. This is the one food which can be absorbed immediately into the blood stream. The advice, "Eat plenty of green vegetables" has a sound scientific basis as well as a decided practical value. The above information is used by special permission from Doctor Jensen.

That all forms of life are interrelated is a statement that very few people will contradict today. Fundamentally, it means that whatever affects plants and the so-called lower animals will have an ultimate bearing on human welfare, as well. The "Back to Nature"—organically grown food movement—illustrates this principle in no uncertain manner.

In California, there is a Health-Food store, one of whose specialties is "eggs from contented hens." That is not an imaginary statement, nor an exaggeration. On the ranch where the health foods are grown, everything is raised by organic gardening. Their flocks of chickens are comfortably housed in clean, spacious quarters—not crowded together in small coops. They are fed on Nature's products, seeds, and herbs untainted by chemical additives that are supposed to increase egg production. The result? Egg production is extremely high, the year around. The eggs are extra large with wonderful flavor, and—this is the amazing part —every egg has a double yolk! Of course they cost more, but they are worth it. One can still buy them by the dozen rather than by the pound.

173

Another application in the use of herb sprouts in nutrition, exemplifying the almost magical effect of chlorophyll, has been reported from the operations at certain agricultural colleges. In their research departments, they have constructed specially designed "incubators," where grass seeds, including oats, have been grown by hydroponics— that is, in special culture media (organically, of course) and green grass has been made available the year around, not just during the growing season. By feeding this to cattle, milk production has been increased during the entire year. The cattle were reported to be as healthy and productive in the winter as they are in spring and summer. Reports from some farmers show that milk production has been from 10% to 20% higher than it was with pasture grass. Herbs benefit animals as well as mankind.

In further proof of the statement that meals consisting of herbs and herbal products can be furnished which will provide all food constituents, the following menus are reproduced from the book by Dr. Bernard Jensen. They are all examples of meals served at the ranch.

"Tahini" is simply liquefied sesame seeds, with nothing added or subtracted. It has approximately the same consistency as peanut butter. In some countries, particularly in Europe, it is widely used as a substitute for butter and in many cases as an ingredient in other foods.

Tahini can be mixed with honey and milk powder to make a delicious Health Food candy. It is of cream consistency, but it can be hardened by letting it dry out in the refrigerator for a few days. This can be mixed with fruit or nuts to suit individual taste.

174

Tahini butter can also be mixed with milk powder and honey and frozen, to make a very delicious ice cream, which is highly nutritious. Since sesame seeds are fifty percent oil, Tahini butter may be used in place of other shortening, although twice as much is required.

By analysis, 100 grams of sesame seeds contain the following ingredients: Protein, 18.6%; Carbohydrates, 21.6%; Fat, 49.1%; Linoleic Acid, 21 mg; Thiamin, 0.98 mg; Riboflavin, 0.24 mg; Niacin, 5.4 mg. Because of its high nutritive value, it is one of the best herb foods we can eat.

Sesame seed milk can be made by using ¼ cup of sesame seeds to 2 cups of water (or raw goat's milk or cow's milk may be used in place of water, if so desired.) This should be liquefied in blender for one or two minutes, until very fine. It can be filtered if necessary, through cheesecloth to remove the hulls. Fruit juices or other flavoring may be added, to suit the taste. Sesame seed milk may also be made by beating Tahini and water together, thoroughly.

A delicious Sesame Cream can be made using 1 cup of sesame seeds and 1 cup of warm water. Blend these together until very smooth. Filter through cheesecloth if necessary, and add one tablespoonful of honey and a dash of pure vanilla. Blend again until thoroughly mixed and very smooth. Many uses will be found for this nutritious cream as a dressing.

The value of Sesame Oil has been demonstrated many times in history as a source of all the food ingredients. It has a pleasant flavor and is excellent for use as a cooking oil or a salad oil or as a shortening.

A very tasteful salad is made with one head of Romaine

lettuce, one cucumber, three tomatoes and two cups of bean sprouts, with radishes to garnish, and Sesame Cream dressing. Place Romaine lettuce leaves on a salad plate. On these put a layer of bean sprouts. Then slice alternate layers of cucumber and tomatoes over them, tapering to a peak with the last layer cucumber. Garnish this with sliced radishes, and top with the dressing. Use any salad dressing you prefer. However, the Sesame Cream dressing is excellent.

A tossed salad, the flavor of which makes it favorable for any occasion, may be called TOSSED GREEN AND SPROUT SALAD, and it includes the following herbs: Six leaves of Romaine lettuce, several sprigs of Watercress, one green Onion, sliced very thinly, one cup of Alfalfa Sprouts, one shredded Carrot, ¼ cup of finely chopped Chicory, ¼ cup of chopped Parsley and your favorite Salad Dressing.

Tear the leaves of lettuce gently into a salad bowl which has been well rubbed with garlic. Add the other ingredients and pour the dressing over. Toss the mixture lightly together and serve it immediately. This will make several liberal servings.

There is nothing more satisfying than a bowl of excellent soup, especially when it is unusual and highly nutritious. Generally it is followed by an entree that adds to its enjoyment. The following recipes are primary favorites at the Health Ranch:

RAW CORN SOUP

Cut 1½ (or more) cups of kernels of corn off the cob, getting the entire kernel if possible. To this, add 2 cups of whole milk (with cream). (Tahini cream makes an excellent addition.) Then add 1 to 2 teaspoonfuls of Vegetable Seasoning and a dash of Paprika.

Blend the mixture thoroughly until it is very smooth. (For an especially bland soup, this may be strained.)

It may be served as a cool soup, or it can be heated over boiling water in a double boiler, just until it reaches serving temperature. Add a piece of sweet butter and garnish with finely chopped parsley. You'll find it is an epicurean's delight.

Another delicious soup is *BARLEY SOUP.*

Soak two cups of *UNPEARLED BARLEY* in water overnight. Use spring water, if possible, to avoid the chlorination that most city water has. After soaking, *almost* cook it, but do not boil it.

Chop one medium-sized onion very fine, one cup of celery, also chopped fine, and one-half cup of finely chopped green pepper. Add this mixture to the barley, using more water if necessary. Now cook this until tender, but avoid unnecessary violent boiling. Before serving, add one tablespoonful of sweet butter and some sweet cream.

If a cream soup is desired, this may be puréed in the blender. If you so desire, a little vegetable seasoning may be added before serving. *Unpearled* Barley is best, because the "pearling process" removes most of the vitamins.

LIMA BEAN CHOWDER is another favorite at the Health Ranch:

Take 1 cup of *barely cooked* dried Lima Beans, 1 cup of diced Turnip, 1 small (or medium-sized) Onion, thinly sliced, and ½ clove of Garlic, chopped fine. Combine these in enough water to cover. Then add more water if necessary and cook until all the ingredients are tender. To this cooked mixture, add one cup of milk (Sesame Seed Milk will give a delicious flavor), two tablespoonfuls of sweet butter and two teaspoonfuls of Vegetable shortening. Mix thoroughly and heat through without boiling. Finely chopped Parsley makes a wonderful garnish.

One of the most delicious of the foods recommended by Doctor Jensen is:

VEGETABLE CHOP SUEY

Heat one-half cup of Soy or Safflower Oil in a large skillet. Add three large green peppers, sliced, one cup of thinly sliced Onions, two cups of sliced Celery, and three cups of Bean Sprouts; mix and sauté for two minutes. Then add 1 cup of Boiling Water and Vegetable Seasoning to taste; cover and cook about eight minutes. Prepare ¼ cup of Arrowroot, two tablespoons of Soy Powder, two teaspoons of Soy Sauce and a little water and mix it to a paste; then stir the paste into the vegetables. Cook for about two minutes. This Chop Suey preparation should be served hot, over *Unpolished* Rice or Wholegrain Noodles. It is a preparation fit for royalty. More Soy Sauce may be added to suit your taste.

BEAN LOAF is an excellent vegetable entree. To 2 cups of Beans, cooked, with their liquor, add 1 Egg, well beaten; 1 cup of Wholegrain Breadcrumbs, 1 tbsp of finely minced Onion, 1 cup of finely diced Celery, 2 tsp of Vege-

178

table Seasoning, and 1 cup of Tomato Pulp. Mix these thoroughly and shape into a loaf. Bake in a moderate oven (300 to 350 degrees) for half an hour.

Another unusual recipe which produces a preparation that has a zest all its own is *RICE À LA POLYNESIAN.*

Mix together one and one-half cups of unpolished Brown Rice which has been parboiled, one and one-half cups of diagonally-sliced Celery, one fourth cup of finely minced Onion and one and one half cups of Peas, either fresh or frozen. Transfer this mixture to a casserole. Then prepare two cups of vegetable broth or water, one tablespoon of Soy Sauce, one tablespoon of Vegetable Seasoning, one teaspoon of either Raw Sugar or Honey and one teaspoon of Sea Salt. Bring this latter mixture to a boil, then pour it over the Casserole Mixture. Cover and bake for 30 minutes. Then stir it, remove the lid and bake for another 15 minutes. This should be served hot, possibly with toast made with wholegrain bread.

Doctor Jensen claims that the following recipe is his favorite: *WILD RICE SOUFFLÉ.*

For best results, the directions for mixing the ingredients should be followed conscientiously.

To One Cup of Wild Rice, which has been washed thoroughly with pure water, add one and one-half cups of water and *simmer* this until it is tender. Do not boil this violently. Then set this aside for use later.

Dice one Green Onion (including the green top) and dice one stalk of Celery. Add one-third cup of water. WILT THIS.

179

Separate the Whites and Yolks of four Eggs, and set aside. Now combine the Wild Rice with the Onions and Celery and add one tablespoon of melted Butter.

Blend in (off heat) one tablespoon Arrowroot and one-half teaspoon Sea Salt.

Add gradually one-half cup of Milk, creaming until smooth.

Now cook the mixture in a double boiler, stirring until it is thick.

Now beat the Egg Yolks and slowly add, while stirring. Now COOL the Mixture. Then add one-half teaspoon of finely chopped Sweet Basil, (either fresh or dried) to the Vegetables and Wild Rice.

Carefully cut in the stiffly beaten Egg Whites. Mix lightly but thoroughly.

Pour into ungreased casserole, stand in a pan of hot water and bake in slow oven (300 degrees) for 1½ hours or until set. SERVE IMMEDIATELY.

Herbalism includes not only the study of herbs themselves, but also a consideration of herbal products. Honey is a typical example of a herbal product. It is manufactured from herbal and flower nectar by the intricate and wonderful chemistry of Nature in the bee's body, so it may be said to be directly a product of the herbs, themselves. The same principle applies to milk, sugar, and eggs. Each of these is produced directly from herbs, by Nature's chemistry—not by man-made synthesis. Therefore, in any study of Herbalism, they are definitely Herbal Products.

A   delicious   *SELF-LEAVENING   CORN-SESAME*

BREAD is made by taking one part of Yellow Corn Meal and one part of Sesame Seed Meal and mixing in cold water to make a rather liquid batter. Bake this until done in a moderate oven, using a Pyrex glass baking dish for the best results. This makes a soft, nutritious and tasty food that is almost like cake! It is non-acid forming and non-gas producing.

UNLEAVENED CORN BREAD is made by mixing 2 cups of Yellow Cornmeal, 1 tbsp of Vegetable Seasoning, 2 tbsp of Raw Sugar (or Honey, if desired) 2 tbsp Wholewheat Flour and warming the mixture. To this add 2 cups of Boiling Water and 4 tbsp of Vegetable Shortening. Then stir in 2 Egg Yolks. Beat 2 Egg Whites and fold in. Bake the mixture in a hot oven.

CHIA CEREAL. This may be an innovation to many, but it's really delicious. One tablespoonful of Chia seed, either whole or ground, is added to one-half cup of water. Stir, let it stand a few minutes and stir again. Let the seed soak for several hours, or overnight. It's ready to use. Eat it as you do other cereal, adding fruit, honey, or whatever you prefer; or, it can be warmed over hot water.

A delicious *SWEET SANDWICH FILLING* is made by mixing Sunflower Seed MEAL to a thick paste with Honey and spreading it generously on lightly toasted Corn Bread or Wholegrain toast. This may be varied by using half Sunflower Seed Meal and half Tahini. Other variations may suggest themselves to suit your taste.

Also, the above mixtures may be used to make a delicious "Taste Teaser."

181

STUFFED CELERY

Cut fresh, tender, firm Celery stalks into two-inch sections. Stuff them liberally with Tahini alone, or with a mixture of Tahini and Sunflower Seed Meal, or pure Peanut Butter. Other combinations may suggest themselves.

CANTALOUPE COCKTAIL

Take one-half cup of SEEDS and the juice from the center of a Cantaloupe. To this add one cup of UNSWEET-ENED PINEAPPLE JUICE. Blend this mixture until it is very fine. It may be strained through cheesecloth if desired. Serve it cold, as a very delicious, nutritious natural cocktail.

A wonderful *HIGH-PROTEIN DRINK* is made as follows:

To two cups of Skimmed Milk add four rounded Tbsp of Soy Powder, two Tbsp of Blackstrap Molasses, four rounded Tbsp of Non-Fat Dry Milk, two Raw Eggs, and Pure Vanilla to taste. Blend this mixture in the liquefier until it is smooth. HONEY may be added for extra sweetening.

From the dim, distant past up to the customs of modern times, it will be noted that Herbs and Herbal Products have played an outstanding role in human welfare. The increasing popularity of modern "Health Foods" is an indication that thinking people are realizing that, after all, Nature Knows Best.

182

CHAPTER TWELVE

Food, Medicine, and Pleasure

IF ONE APPROACHES THE STUDY OF HERBALISM seriously, with open mind, with eagerness to learn, and willingness to accept evidence of legend, folklore, and history, then certain conclusions are inevitable. America is the land of opportunity. Today's civilization also exemplifies the fact that we are the Melting Pot of the Nations of the World.

All immigrants who come to our shores have certain racial traits, habits of thought and action, and innate customs that differentiate them from other people. However, association, economic necessity, and time will blend these differences into a citizenry that is "typically American" whose ideal is Freedom and the Equality of Opportunity. Realization of that Ideal has made America a leading World Power.

However, it must be realized that the blending process does not destroy individual characteristics. It merely absorbs them into a new pattern where their value will add to the total. Perhaps an analogy will illustrate this contribution of factors to give desired results.

America leads in producing numerous grades of steel to suit every purpose. The number and variety of special steels has increased at an almost unbelievable rate. Vast industrial foundries have expanded to meet the demands. The science and art of steel making can be compared to the assimilation of new citizens into our body politic.

The raw materials are Iron Ore, Pig Iron, scrap steel, and a "flux"—(possibly limestone). These are put into the bed of an electric arc furnace and the current turned on. The intense heat of the electric arc quickly melts the mixture. A sample of the "melt" is taken at the furnace, cooled, and rushed to the laboratory. Immediately all is action. The control chemist makes a rapid determination of Carbon in the melt, and telephones the result to the chief melter at the furnace. In fifteen or twenty minutes another sample is received and the rapid determination tells the chemist and the melter how fast the reducing action is progressing. Meanwhile, the chemist is making or has made an analysis for Silicon, Manganese, Sulfur, Phosphorus, and possibly Nickel and Chromium, if the scrap steel was an alloy. When a series of such tests shows that the Carbon content of the melt has reached the low level desired, the chemist calculates the weight of Petroleum Coke necessary to bring the percentage of carbon in the finished steel to the desired point, and also the amount of Ferrosilicon, Ferromanganese, Metallic Nickel, Metallic Copper, Ferrochrome, Vanadium, Tungsten, Titanium, or other alloy materials necessary to meet the specifications for the finished steel.

These additions, alloys, or compounds do not lose their

individual identity in the melting process. Each element has its own characteristics. The Chromium in Ferro-Chrome retains its properties as Chromium. The Ferro-Vanadium adds the properties which Vanadium can give to the steel. And so on throughout the list. Every added material that is finally in the total melt furnishes necessary properties that will bring the finished steel up to the specifications for the purpose required.

So it is with the immigrants to America. Each individual is endowed with certain racial traits that are not lost in the naturalization process. These characteristics are merely blended with others of various groups to make the "annealing process" from which the typical American Citizen emerges.

Nowhere is this retention of racial habits and preferences more noticeable than in the matter of food and cooking.

The following comments and descriptions are not taken from any published books or articles. They are the result of personal contacts and observations. It was our privilege to spend several months in and around New Orleans and Louisiana, and to talk with many of the descendants of the early settlers of that territory. Some of the modern usages show very little change from the days of the earliest settlement.

Undoubtedly the French were the first white settlers in the territory surrounding the lower Mississippi and its delta. Many of them came down the River from northern settlements to join those who arrived by the Gulf route.

185

Racial instinct caused them to build homes in this land of fertility, forests, and water.

That many early settlers, or even the majority of them came from the north-central part of France, from the old Provinces of Île-de-France which is the territory surrounding Paris and the Province of Orléanais immediately to the southwest, is proved by two facts. The first is based on tradition and language similarity and general racial characteristics. The second is that the baby colony was given the name "New Orleans." It was as if they were memorializing their former home. The original settlement was familiarly known as *"Le Vieux Carré"* (The Old Square) and even today the French Quarter is often referred to as The Old Square. It is famous the world over for many things.

Historically, New Orleans, from 1717 until the American Revolution in 1776, was typically Provincial France transplanted to America. The Spanish infiltrated, and in some respects usurped control, but the basic racial habits persisted, particularly with reference to the food situation. The prolific use of herbs in daily diet by French chefs was a distinguishing mark in those early days as well as today.

Someone has said that history is the product of legends and folklore often repeated and then practiced. That is especially true in regard to individual characteristics of many nationalistic groups in various parts of America—notably the French in Quebec, Montreal, and New Orleans, the Italians in Boston, New York, San Francisco, and other large cities. Also German and Dutch communities in Pennsylvania and elsewhere evidence the influence of national traditions. Individual customs are pronounced in the Scandinavian settlements in Wisconsin, Minnesota, the Dakotas, Montana, and the Northwest. The Spanish influence is quite dominant in California, Arizona, and parts of Texas and New Mexico. All of these widely distributed people who have chosen America as their home, however, agree in one particular action-pattern: the use of herbs and herbal products in the preparation of their food.

To the majority of people, the mention of French cooking conjures mental images of gustatory enjoyment. That well-deserved reputation has been earned through centuries of practice by French housewives and professional chefs. From early provincial days to the present time, the oftentimes unexpressed ideal of a meal has been a combination of two related factors—nutrition and pleasure. It is more than a science; it is an art. Psychologists tell us that repeated sensations develop into attention, which merges into interest. Then comes action, from which habits are formed.

In early life, French girls are instructed in the art of food preparation. Whether they like it or not, it becomes a habit. All French housewives instinctively know the secret which makes French meals both delightful and nutritious. Is there a special formula which must be learned during years of trial and error? No. The answer is really quite simple. Probably more than any other national group, French cooks have developed the use of herbs and herbal products in all phases of the preparation of foods. That includes soups, *Hors-d'Oeuvre,* the various *Entrees* and

187

Desserts, even beverages were given extra delicate flavoring by special herbal additions.

During our sojourn in New Orleans, we were privileged to consult with several French people who were direct descendants of the original settlers. One young lady said, "But yes, my great-great-great grandfather was one of the original pioneer settlers of New Orleans. He built a home in the Vieux Carré on Rue de Bourbon. That home is still standing, although it has been repaired many times. The balcony and patio are much the same as they were in the old days, I have been told."

"Can you tell me something about your life, and the habits of the people?" I asked. We were standing in front of a display counter in one of New Orleans' largest department stores.

"But yes. Me, I'm just a clerk in this store. It's a wonderful store, and I meet many interesting people. But my hobby, outside of my work, is cooking. I like to make good things to eat. We have our own herb garden, and you know we French people are noted for the clever use of herbs in the preparation of food."

"Can you describe your herb garden?"

"Better yet. It's almost closing time. If you would like to come home with me, I'll show you the garden, and then we'll have a sample of some real French cooking."

"But that would be putting you to a lot of trouble."

"No trouble at all. Next to cooking, I like to have an appreciative audience."

By the time we reached her home in the French Quarter,

it was too dark to see very much, but she promised to give me a diagram of the garden. Then we went into the house and she turned to me with a suggestion: "I'm hungry. How about you?"

"What you told me about your cooking would give me an appetite, even if I weren't hungry. But I'm looking forward to this experience, and I thank you for the privilege."

"Contrary to a great many women, I like to have an appreciative audience when I cook. So if you want to watch me, I'll be happy."

On shelves above her kitchen work bench, arranged in alphabetical order, were large jars, each filled with an herb. She noticed our interest and commented, "Those are the ones I use most frequently. There are others that I use fresh from the garden, in season, and I can some for winter use. I use potatoes all the time, and onions, and garlic, in addition to the ones you see here."

She continued to work while she talked. "This meal I'm preparing now is one of my favorites. The French name for it is LÉGUMES À LA GRECQUE. That means MARINATED VEGETABLES, GREEK STYLE. It's an old recipe that dates away back to Provincial France. The marinade has to be prepared ahead of time, so I did that last night. It's quite simple to prepare. I use 3 cups of chicken stock (some people call it chicken broth), 1 cup of dry white wine—either sauterne or chablis. I prefer chablis. 1 cup of olive oil. You could use peanut oil or safflower oil. It might make a little difference in the taste. About ½ cup of

189

lemon juice or wine vinegar, half a dozen sprigs of parsley; one or two cloves of garlic, cut up quite fine, about ½ teaspoon of dried thyme and 10 peppercorns. Salt the mixture —perhaps using about 1 teaspoon. I stir all these together in a large stainless steel saucepan. After it just boils, I cover the pan, reduce the heat and simmer for 45 minutes; then I strain it through a very fine sieve, and press the solids with the back of a spoon or fork, to be sure the juices are all out. Sometimes it takes a lot of pressure. Then I usually discard the solids. The liquid marinade should taste a little over-seasoned.

"It's time now for the final putting together process. Bring the liquid marinade just to boiling and add the onions. Put the cover on the saucepan and cook at reasonable heat for half an hour. By that time the onions will be just tender. Then I take a sieve or a slotted spoon and remove the onions and put them into another stainless steel container.

"The marinade should be just simmering by this time, but not boiling hard. I add the sliced zucchini and squash and I cook them slowly for about 15 minutes. Then they go into the baking dish with the onions. During the cooking of the zucchini and squash, they shouldn't be covered.

"Now I add all the other vegetables—last night I put in celery hearts, mushrooms, cucumbers, string beans, and artichoke hearts. I gave them the same treatment, with the marinade, then they all went into the baking dish.

"The next treatment is very important. I brought the marinade just to a boil and poured it over the vegetables, making sure that they were covered or at least wet with the hot liquid. Then I covered the dish with aluminum foil and put it in the refrigerator overnight. That is when the real marinating process actually takes place.

"Now comes the final stage." She removed the foil from the baking dish that she had taken from the refrigerator. Very carefully she lifted the vegetables and placed them artistically on a serving platter, and garnished it with sprigs of fresh parsley and slices of lemon. "There! It's all ready for you to enjoy!"

It was enjoyable to look at and the taste was delicious beyond description.

"It's too dark now for you to see the herb garden," she continued, "but I'll give you a diagram of it. You understand that the ones I grow in this garden are the specials that I use for extra flavoring or for a particular effect, either in taste or appearance. The commoner ones, such as potatoes, tomatoes, garlic, carrots, parsnips, onions, lettuce, yams, beets, peas, beans, turnips, rutabagas, celery, cabbage, cucumbers, or others one can buy in the market the year around, both in season and out of season. There's a word of caution about vegetables in the market. Be sure you're not buying material that has had insect spray used on it. That's bad. No matter how much you wash it, you can't get it all off."

As she began to draw the diagram, she said, "I don't suppose it makes much difference about the arrangement of the beds. You'll notice I have all my members of the mint family at one side. That's for convenience.

191

"Next I have Parsley and its relative, Chervil, both good as garnishes and in salads and soups; also Chive, with the onion-like flavor that adds zest to salads and soups. Then there's Oregano; that is used a great deal in Italian-type cooking, for its aromatic, strong flavor, particularly with tomatoes or eggplant or with meat dishes.

"The herbs of the Mint family I favor especially, as you'll notice: Marjoram is quite strong and aromatic, with just enough bitterness to give it distinction. Savory, traditionally excellent for adding zest to peas or beans, with its warmth, is a favorite of mine. Basil is always popular and refreshing. I always use it with tomatoes, either raw or cooked. It's also good with fish or any sea food, or with eggs. Sage is familiar to all as an ingredient of stuffing mixtures and dressings, and to add an agreeable flavor to roast pork or sausage.

"Rosemary is an herb that should be used sparingly, because when it is heated, it emits a strong oil. But it gives a wonderful flavor to meat dishes.

"Then there's Tarragon. Some people say it smells a little like Licorice. Mixed with other herbs, it adds a delicious flavor. I also use it a lot for sea food and for chicken.

"The next one is Fennel. That's another herb that has an odor faintly licorice-like. Many people eat the roots and stalks of Fennel raw or cooked. I use its leaves, which are almost lacelike, and the seeds and stems to give a wonderful flavor to soups, sauces, and salads.

"I always have my bed of red radishes. Sliced thin, diced or grated, everybody knows how wonderfully they fit into any salad. Of course they are delicious just to eat raw, with or without salt.

"Little green onions are familiar to all who like good food. Here in the South, we can raise most of the herbs out of doors the year around. But one can have an herb garden even in the North—in window boxes or other sheltered places.

"The last two that I have in my garden, strawberries and asparagus, often take a couple of years to get well started.

THE DIAGRAM OF AN HERB GARDEN

(It is understood that this plan may be varied to suit individual needs. Other herbs may be added to suit convenience and circumstances.)

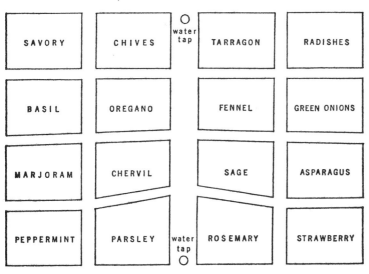

But their value is often beyond description. They can be used in so many ways.

"If one has plenty of space, and also the time to do it right, an herb garden is one of the most satisfying hobbies I know and it will keep growing in interest as you add or substitute.

"Another point that I believe is important. I always use organic fertilizer—never the commercial mixtures. Also, I rotate the beds, so I don't have just one crop depleting the soil year after year. Any questions?"

"There are many questions I could ask, but you've already given a lot of your time, and we appreciate it. You're putting your knowledge and your hobby to a wonderful use. No wonder French cooking is considered so magnificent."

THE FRENCH-ITALIAN-MEDITERRANEAN INFLUENCE

Living in retirement in Southern California, a gentlemen who likes to call himself "an old cook," often tells about his experiences when he was chef in exclusive establishments in various cities including Hollywood and Los Angeles. One of the preparations for which he was famous, he calls, "FRENCH-ITALIAN VEGETABLE SOUP." We are reproducing the recipe just as he told it. The modern name for it is "MINESTRONE."

"In the first place don't try to rush this. Take plenty of time. Have all the ingredients ready before you begin.

194

You'll need a couple of four-quart saucepans, a large bowl, a two-gallon soup pot or kettle, a slotted spoon and some paper towels, also two or three dishes large enough to hold the vegetables as they are prepared before the final mix.

"In a gallon-size saucepan, I boil a quart of water so it's just bubbling. Into that, I put ½ cup of beans. I usually use navy, or white kidney. If you want to use pintos or regular kidneys, it might make a slight difference in the taste. Then raise the heat and boil very briskly for two or three minutes. Then remove the pan from the heat and let the beans soak in the water for an hour. After that, put the pan back on the stove, turn the heat to 'Simmer,' and let it cook for an hour and a half, uncovered. By that time, the beans will be just tender.

"While the beans are cooking, prepare the other ingredients. Notice that the following materials are all herbs except ½ cup of diced salt pork, 2 quarts of chicken stock (chicken broth) and the salt. (Even Cheese can be considered an herbal product, because cheese comes from milk and milk is produced because the cows eat herbs.) You will need, besides at least 4 tbsp butter or margarine:

Two cups of drained, whole-pack tomatoes, that have been coarsely chopped; 1 cup of fresh green peas; 1 cup of diced, unpeeled zucchini that has been scrubbed thoroughly; 1 cup of diced potatoes; 1 cup of diced carrots; 2 tablespoons very finely chopped onions and ¼ cup of finely chopped leeks. If you can't get the leeks, add another ¼ cup of onions instead. Then ½ to 1 cup of very thinly sliced celery. Now we'll need ½ cup of diced salt pork and two quarts of chicken stock. That can be either fresh or canned. Then I have one bay leaf and two parsley sprigs, tied together. To this vegetable mixture, I add about a teaspoon of salt and some ground black pepper. I also have ½ cup of raw rice to use as a final addition. Some chefs use white rice, but I prefer brown rice on account of its higher vitamin content.

"The canned Minestrone that you buy in the markets is very good, an excellent imitation of the 'supervariety' that I make, but it still lacks that 'something' that loving care will give. You understand what I mean?

"Now comes the important process of putting everything together to make the delicious finished product. Melt the butter or margarine in a skillet. When it stops foaming, add the potatoes, peas, zucchini, carrots, and celery. Using a wooden spoon, toss them thoroughly for about three minutes, until the vegetables are all covered. Do not brown them. Then set them to one side, off the heat.

"Fry the salt pork which has been diced, in the soup kettle, to render the fat. When the pork is crisped, and browned, after stirring it over moderate heat, remove the diced meat with a coarse sieve or a slotted spoon, and place it on paper towels to drain. Stir the onions and leeks in the fat remaining in the kettle. Stir constantly and cook for approximately five minutes, or until the onions are soft and browned slightly.

"Now stir in the coarsely chopped tomatoes, the chicken stock and the vegetables from the skillet; also the bay leaf and parsley, a little salt and pepper. Now is the time to

196

bring the soup mixture to a boil, over high heat. Then reduce the heat and simmer partially covered, for about half an hour. Then remove the bay leaf and parsley. Now add the rice, beans, and salt pork. Cook it for 20 minutes more, or until the rice is tender.

"At this point, I always taste the soup, and add a little salt and pepper if it is necessary. It's now ready to be served, in the individual bowls. A good finishing touch is to sprinkle a finely divided herb mixture or garnish on top. For this, I blend together two teaspoons of pulverized dried basil—or one tablespoon of fresh basil chopped very fine, one tablespoon of very finely chopped fresh parsley and ½ teaspoon of finely divided garlic. I always have a bowl of grated cheese handy, so if one wants it, it's ready.

"This is not merely a soup appetizer, but it's an entire meal in itself, and a very nourishing one. Every herb used adds a definite flavor to the finished product."

America is rapidly becoming "Herb Conscious." Even confirmed meat eaters know that the juiciest, most appetizing meat comes from animals that have been fed on selected grains. All the common grains are herbs. Frequently the newspapers publish comments showing the increasing value placed on herbs and herbal products. This dispatch appeared in a recent issue of a California newspaper:

MONTGOMERY, Ala. (UPI)
—Alabama's vegetable-producing industry is grossing $20 million a year and may become one of the state's major agricultural businesses.
During the past year, there were 10,000 acres of

fresh market tomatoes, and acreage for processing crops, such as peas, peppers, and cucumbers, was well over 5000 acres each.

That, of course was in addition to all other farm crops, most of which are herbs. And this was from only one state out of fifty!

Even earlier than recorded history, herbs and herbal products have been the main source of food for the developing nations of the world. When the pioneers from Europe came to America in early Colonial times, they brought with them their legends, folklore and food preferences which they added to the existing Indian herbs and methods of food preparation, gradually to build up the modern cuisine. That will vary, of course, according to the food habits of each nationalistic group.

Undoubtedly the French have had more influence than any other nationalistic group in building the food tastes of modern America. That is true for two main reasons: first, because they use many herbs in their cooking, not only for the nutritive value, but also for the nuances of delicate flavor so characteristic of French food preparation; in the second place, Americans like novelty, and the mere mention of French cooking conjures up gustatory visions of gourmet enjoyment.

But Italian food, esoteric Greek preparations, hearty German meals, Scandinavian delicacies, and others occupy a warm place in the food enjoyment of the average American. Add all this together, and we have an expanding interest in herbs and herbal products as food.

198

There is another factor, however, which is more potent than all others in developing genuine enthusiasm for the use of herbs as food. The Pure Food movement is gaining adherents in all parts of America in amazing numbers. In practically every city one can find a Health-Food store, where foods—mostly herbs—are featured that are the product of organic gardening, eliminating the dangers of commercial fertilizers and insecticides. The herbs sold in these stores are especially grown to augment their natural vitamin content. They are guaranteed to be free from artificial treatment or insecticides.

The American people are at last coming to realize that we are slowly killing ourselves chemically, in the name of "progress," by our almost fanatical reliance on the highly advertised synthetic food products. These foods undoubtedly have many merits. Of course they meet the requirements of the Pure Food Laws, or they could not be sold on the open markets. But, as has been stated by eminent nutrition authorities, there is a vast difference between synthetic chemical mixtures and Nature's offerings. We are sure that herbs grown by organic gardening, unpolluted by poisonous chemical insecticides, are pure and nutritious. The wise course for us to pursue is to follow Nature's teachings. The main difficulty in today's economy is that people have the almighty dollar so close to their eyes that they can't see around it!

A few years ago, it was the author's privilege to live and work in a Finnish community in Montana. We found the people very cooperative, sincere, and alert. While they were clannish, as was to be expected, they fraternized well with others in the village and surrounding area. One outstanding feature, however, was especially noticeable. The folklore and racial traditions were an integral part of their daily lives. While this might be considered deleterious to a certain extent, from an extremely modern viewpoint, nevertheless it was and is a strong factor in the superior character of these additions to our American body politic. It gives solidarity and stamina of decision, which is needed in today's world-unrest.

Good health and long life are two ideals which these citizens cherish, and they rightly attribute both to food preparation and quality. The answer of course is HERBS! Crops are grown organically, and herbs and herbal products constitute the bulk of their daily diet. More than that; their neighbors are developing like habits of food selection. There were two particular food preparations that were prime favorites and which were adopted by their neighbors. It should be noted that both recipes stress herbs.

In speaking Finnish words, each letter is pronounced at its full value. If consonants or vowels are doubled, syllabication comes between the duplicate letters. For example, the Finnish name for Turnip or Rutabaga Casserole is *LÄNT-TULA-ATIK-KO*. The ingredients are simple, all herbs or herbal products. The vegetable casserole can be used either to accompany a meat entree or as a meal in itself. The preparation is quite simple. We have watched it, and have partaken of the delicious results.

Depending on the number to be served, the Finnish

housewife took two or three medium-sized rutabagas, or the equivalent in turnips, washed them, and diced them into small, quarter-inch cubes. Natural gas had not yet been piped into the community, so she preheated the wood-burning oven to approximately 350 degrees.

Then she placed the diced turnips in a two-gallon saucepan and just covered the vegetables with cold water. She placed this on top of the stove and added about one teaspoon of salt. Then she remarked, "We like the flavor of onions, so I usually add one small onion, chopped very fine. But that is not necessary." After the mixture comes to a bubbling boil, it is partially covered and allowed to simmer for about twenty minutes. She tested the turnips then with the point of a sharp knife. When assured they were thoroughly soft, she put them into a sieve container, over a bowl and pressed the mass of vegetables through the meshes of the sieve with the back of a wooden spoon. That, of course, was after she had drained the water off.

Meanwhile, in another bowl, she prepared a mixture of three cups of dry breadcrumbs and an equal amount of heavy cream, with about half a teaspoon of nutmeg and a teaspoon of salt and three lightly beaten eggs. When that was smooth, she stirred in the cooked vegetables, and placed the mixture in a buttered three-quart baking dish and dotted the top with bits of butter. This was baked, uncovered, in the oven for a little over an hour, until the top was lightly browned. It can be served with a meat entree or alone.

Another herbal food preparation that was favored by the

201

people in this Finnish community was a delicious vegetable accompaniment to a hearty meal where the main entree was roast meat or fried mountain trout. FRIED MUSH-ROOMS WITH SOUR CREAM DRESSING—the Finnish name for which is *PAI-STE-TUT SI-EN-ET* has a delight-ful flavor all its own. Not only was it a favorite of the Finnish people, but their American neighbors adopted it as a frequent addition to their daily diet, as well.

As we watched the procedure, its preparation was quite simple. In a 12-inch enameled frying pan, or a stainless steel skillet of equal size or larger, she put eight table-spoons of margarine or butter, and melted it over moderate heat. After the melt had finished foaming, she added about ½ cup of very finely chopped onions and cooked them about five or six minutes. Then the onions were transpar-ent, but they were not browned.

While the onions were cooking, she sliced two pounds of mushrooms very thin. When the onions were soft and transparent, the sliced mushrooms were added, gradually, with constant stirring, using a wooden spoon, so that the mushrooms and onions were blended well. The frying con-tinued for five minutes or more, until the mushrooms were slightly brown. The mixture was stirred occasionally, to prevent sticking. Then a cup of fine, dry breadcrumbs was sprinkled over the mixture and the contents were stirred gently with a wooden spoon. After this, the frying pan was removed from the hot part of the stove.

Then, in another bowl, she put a cup of sour cream and beat or whipped it with a wooden spoon briskly for a couple of minutes, after which she stirred it into the vege-

202

table mixture in the skillet, until the mushrooms were all coated with the cream. Then it was ready to serve. This delicious preparation can be used as a snack in itself, or to accompany meat or fish dinners.

Since the population of America is made up of many different nationalities, it is understandable that each group has contributed to the total culture of our modern life. No other country in the world has as varied an ancestral background as the United States of America. From the earliest days of colonization to the selective quota of immigrants today, the new arrivals have brought and are bringing with them their folklore, traditions, habits of life, and customs that may be modified, but not radically changed by their new environment. Our modern science, daily habits, thoughts, and ambitions are a composite or a blending of the folklore, traditions, and racial habits of the people who have made America a great nation.

Of the three essentials for human existence—air, water, and food—the first two, air and water, are universal. Food, however, and the food habits of people and animals, are determined by custom and availability. From the earliest times, throughout history, the use of herbs, herbal products, and herbal derivatives has constituted the major portion of food requirements.

It is natural to think of herbs as connected with food. However, it must be realized that modern medicine is a development of the earliest use of herbs in ancient Egypt and Greece for their healing effects. The Indians in the Americas also gave us a heritage of the use of herbs for medicinal purposes.

PART FOUR

EPILOGUE

For Reference and Information

TO LIST ALL OF THE PLANTS THAT CAN BE botanically classified as herbs would be a stupendous task and such a list would include many which up to the present time have no recognized practical use. It is beneficial, however, to mention those which are so common that many people do not think of them as herbs, and then describe briefly some of the special herbs that give particular flavor to foods, or which are especially valuable for their medicinal characteristics. There are many which are interesting from a historical as well as a utilitarian viewpoint.

The common cereal grains are the seeds of herbs. Barley, corn, popcorn, oats, wheat, rice, millet, rye, buckwheat, and other foods thought of as "breakfast cereals" are excellent foods, particularly if they have not been subjected to chemical processing or insecticide treatment. They are too familiar to warrant special description.

The common vegetables, such as potatoes, sweet potatoes, yams, tomatoes, carrots, parsnips, turnips, rutabagas, peas, and the many varieties of beans are all herbs. To continue with the list, we have onions, leeks, chard, and the other leafy vegetables used as greens, beets, parsley, lettuce, celery, radishes, horseradish, chive, rhubarb, cabbage, kale, cucumbers, kohlrabi, and others. The use of any or all of these is a matter of our daily habits. A meal without herbs would be almost a curiosity. In addition to the common ones mentioned, there are certain ones that may well be noted, for their particular flavor. These are usually grown in a special herb garden.

If one is contemplating an experimental herb garden some suggestions will be advantageous. There are no set rules, either as to size, arrangement, or selection. Detailed plans are naturally dependent on availability of space or other matters of convenience. City dwellers or those who live in apartments without yards can have an indoor garden, using flower pots for individual plants. If you live in the suburbs or in the country, larger plots are possible. There is much satisfaction in developing even a small garden. Regardless of size, certain essentials are important.

Moisture and good drainage are necessary. A good sandy-loam soil is required. Any fertilizer used should be organic—well-rotted, pulverized manure or compost. If the soil is not naturally alkaline, hydrated lime and/or wood ashes will be indicated. Avoid commercial chemical fertilizers. Careful preparation of the soil may determine the difference between success or failure. Since most herbs are treasured for their leaves, with the exception of cereal grains, which are seeds, a high humus or nitrogen content should be present in the soil. Otherwise leaves will not re-

208

main green, but will turn yellow, or wither. While a good leaf growth is desirable, care must be taken not to have plants go to an excess in that respect, which would result in diluting or dissipating the essential oils.

If an out-of-doors garden is planned, the bed should be prepared in the autumn, particularly if fertilizer or compost is used. Preparing the ground in the fall will enrich the topsoil during the winter months, which will more adequately benefit spring planting. It also makes the soil more easily worked.

In the list which follows, both the common name and the botanical name are given. Brief directions for planting are also included.

For the Home Herb Garden, a selection from the following list of plants is suggested:

BASIL: There are several varieties of BASIL (Probably the best one is Sweet Basil (*Ocimum basilicum*). It is an annual, and grows from seed. It is extremely sensitive to frost, and should be planted in the spring, after all frost danger is past. After sprouting, the seedlings ought to be thinned to about eight inches apart, for the maturing plant needs that much space for proper growth. Basil is especially good with tomatoes; also it is excellent in salads, in spaghetti sauce, in meat dishes and egg dishes.

BORAGE: (*Borago officinalis*) This is preeminently a salad herb, and also it may be used in cocktails. The use of *young* leaves of this plant in salads or cocktails will give a delicate "cucumbery" flavor. When the leaves get old, they

209

become tough and hairy. It is a hardy annual, and grows well in a temperate climate until the first frost. The blue or lavender star-shaped flowers are beautiful.

BURNET, sometimes called "SALAD BURNET" is botanically known as *Sanguisorba minor*. It is very hardy, and a perennial. It can be planted as early in the spring as the ground can be worked. Or, for earlier maturing, young plants can be started in the early spring. This will provide leaves for early summer salads. If this plant is allowed to go to seed, it will sow itself. The leaves that grow close to the ground usually stay green all winter. For best results, each plant requires about a square foot of space. The leaves give a pleasant, slightly cucumbery flavor to salads, and also they can be used to make herb tea.

CHERVIL: (*Anthriscus cerefolium*). This herb is really a "cousin" of parsley, but the taste is somewhat stronger, and it has an individual flavor. It is much used by French cooks in omelettes. It is a hardy annual. If allowed to go to seed, it will sow itself. The plants should be thinned to about six or eight inches apart. If not allowed to flower, it will grow successive crops of leaves. It is an excellent salad herb, and goes well with meats or fish also.

SWEET CICELY: (*Myrrhis odorata*) is very hardy, a perennial that can withstand some frost. However, it dies down to the ground in extremely cold weather. But it self-sows. It will need at least one and one-half feet of space. The leaves add an anise flavor to green salads. The seeds give a delightful anise flavor to cooked foods, and the

210

roots may also be cooked as a pot herb. So this is one herb that can be used in its entirety.

COSTMARY: (*Chrysanthemum balsamita-var. tanacetoides*) This plant is a hardy perennial. In the early Colonial days, the story goes that churchgoers used to put a sprig of this herb in their Bibles to mark the place, and so the popular name in the olden days was "Bible Leaf"! Costmary is tall, spreading, an excellent salad herb, although it should be used rather sparingly, because it gives quite a strong anise flavor. It is a hardy perennial.

CRESS: (*Barbarea praecox*) This is what is called the "UPLAND" variety. It should not be confused with Watercress or Peppergrass. Peppergrass is *Lepedium sativum.* Upland Cress is a hardy biennial. It will withstand zero winters. Its leaves are very much larger than Watercress. It can be used for flavor, or as a salad by itself. The flavor is similar to that of Watercress.

DILL: (*Anethum graveolens*). This herb is best known as a flavoring material for pickles. Perhaps not so well-known uses are as an ideal flavor for lamb roast or barbecue and for fish. Sprigs, leaves, and seeds of this herb are excellent in cooking. It is a hardy annual, and the seeds should be sown thickly, without thinning.

GARLIC: (*Allium sativum*) This member of the lily family, along with Onions, is subject to much comment, both favorable and unfavorable. When used by the enlightened, experienced cook, garlic-flavored foods can become a gourmet's delight; but its use by the inexperienced or amateur or extremist can produce horrible food concoctions. It is a hardy perennial. A garlic bulb consists of cloves, each of which will produce a plant. These cloves can be planted in the fall or very early in the spring. They should be set about four inches apart, in a trench about an inch deep, and covered with loose soil. Garlic plants will grow to approximately 18 inches high.

LOVAGE: (*Levisticum officinale*) This is a hardy perennial herb with an unusual flavor that is suggestive of the Orient. It needs a rich soil, and is at its best when an organic fertilizer is used. The leaves of this plant, either fresh or dried, may be used very liberally in any recipe that calls for curry. The plants should be set at least a foot apart.

LEMON BALM (MELISSA): (*Melissa officinalis*) This is an interesting hardy perennial herb. A tea made from Melissa leaves, either fresh or dried, has a wonderfully refreshing taste, rather resembling a combination of lemons and mint. It is valuable in salads, in connection with meats, fish, or in combination with mint herbs. The seedlings should be set about 18 inches apart. It is a hardy perennial. It may be grown either from seed, or by propagation in early spring by root division.

SWEET MARJORAM: (*Majorama hortensis*). This herb may be designated as a delicate perennial. It does not like cold weather, so it must be treated as an annual instead of a perennial in regions where the winter temperatures are low. But if it is planted in the early spring, a good yield is assured. The leaves give a delightful flavor to meat dishes, spaghetti sauce, soups, etc. The seeds are rather slow to germinate and the sprouts appear small, but in a few weeks they will seem to shoot upward suddenly. They should be thinned to about 5 inches.

SPEARMINT: (*Mentha spicata*). This is a hardy perennial herb. It seems to be very particular about where it will grow. It likes water, but will not grow where there is a muddy soil. Damp ground, with good drainage, is excellent. The leaves of this herb are used in the drink, mint julep, and in the mint sauce that is favored for lamb recipes, or wherever a mint flavor is indicated. It also has a large commercial potential in the perfume and chewing gum industries, as well as food flavoring. It can be grown from seed, but it usually is developed from "stolons"— which are horizontal stems, whose tips go down into the ground and from which new plants will grow. After a new plant has started, the stolon may be cut between the old plant and the new one. Mint plants die down to the ground with frost, but when spring comes, they develop new horizontal shoots, which become vertical when hot weather arrives. The plants will grow to a height of two or three feet.

NASTURTIUMS: (*Tropaeolum minus*). This is a very sensitive annual. We usually think of Nasturtiums as lovely flowers, and many people do not realize that the leaves and shoots used in salads and as a sweet herb give a zesty tang or flavor. Also, the seeds can be pickled. The dwarf variety should be planted, as the other grows too high and large.

ORIGANUM: (*Origanum vulgare*). This is the English

213

variety. The plant which is native to America is an inferior one, which is sometimes called "Wild Marjoram," but this should not be confused with the genuine Sweet Marjoram. While English Origanum can be grown from seeds, they are difficult to obtain in the United States. Plants can be purchased, however. Each plant needs about a square foot of space for best growth. In ancient Greece, Origanum was referred to as the "Delight of the Mountains." Origanum is adaptable for use in connection with beef recipes, meat loaf, spaghetti sauce, and soups. The flavor is somewhat similar to that of Sweet Marjoram, but possibly a bit stronger.

PARSLEY: (*Petroselinum hortense*) This is a hardy biennial plant. There are two common varieties of this herb —plain-leafed and curly-leafed. There is no difference between them except in looks, so the choice is entirely a matter of individual selection. The curly-leafed variety has perhaps a somewhat more pleasing appearance when it is used as a garnish, but the flavor is the same. Parsley seeds are very slow to germinate. This process can be hastened by soaking the seeds in water for overnight, or perhaps even longer. Parsley has a very long growing season. It can be planted as early as the ground can be worked in the spring, and neither the first frost of fall nor the early freeze of winter will kill it, apparently. The leaves stay green. In very cold weather, however, some of the flavor is lost.

ENGLISH PENNYROYAL: (*Mentha pulegium*). While this herb is a true member of the Mint family, its manner of growth is entirely different from Spearmint, whose growing stalks are erect or perpendicular. Pennyroyal produces stems which are prone on the ground. The leaves are small, less than half an inch long, and have a delightful minty fragrance.

ROSEMARY: (*Rosmarinus officinalis*) This evergreen, aromatic, perennial herb was originally a native of southern France, in the Mediterranean coastal region. It does not like cold weather. Before the first autumn frost it should be potted and brought into the house. The Latin generic name, "Rosmarinus" means "Sea-dew." The flavor which a judicious use of this herb gives to meat recipes or fish is not like any other. It is delicious, outstanding, extremely significant, and unforgettable. Because it is so powerful and lingering, a very small amount only should be used. While it can be grown from seed, it is a slow starter, and much more rapid growth results when plants or cuttings are used. It needs lime as fertilizer because it requires an alkaline soil. Some wood ashes or eggshells may be dug in around the roots, which will provide the correct soil conditions.

SAGE: (*Salvia officinalis*). The use of SAGE as a flavoring herb is well known, universally. This plant is a hardy perennial, and will survive cold winter weather. While it can be raised from seed, the first season's growth is relatively slow. It is really preferable to plant year-old units. The leaves of this herb stay green, with their greenish-gray color, all winter long, and in the spring, the older leaves usually die and fall off. When the new young leaves appear, the plant should be cut back to five or six inches off the ground, as that will result in a soft stem condition for

215

the harvest. This process can be repeated at intervals. Sage is a very important ingredient in the preparation of all stuffing mixtures, and it also is valuable as a tea herb. The strength of sage as a herbal accessory of course determines the advice that it should be used with a great deal of moderation.

SAVORY, SUMMER: (*Satureia hortensis*)—This herb, originally imported from Europe, where it originated, is an annual, and it is extremely sensitive to cold weather, so it should be cultivated only in months that are free from frost. It is grown from seed, and in northern climates the proper time for sowing is the last week in May. The plants are quite tall, and erect. They will grow to a height of perhaps eighteen inches. The growth is branching. It is advisable to sow the seeds thickly, because rain or wind will ruin the growth of the spindly shoots. After they grow taller, they may be thinned to within four inches. This sweet herb has quite a pungent flavor, and is especially good with fish, pork, veal, beef, also with string beans or in salads. In the early days, in Europe and particularly in England, Savory was looked upon as a medicinal herb, good for the digestion.

Another related plant is WINTER SAVORY (*Satureia montana*). It is a hardy perennial. The flavor is much stronger and less agreeable than SUMMER SAVORY.

ROQUETTE (*Eruca sativa*) is used in France both for flavor and as a potherb. It is especially good with lettuce. It is a hardy annual, a member of the mustard family. The flavor of this herb is quite strong, so it should be used

216

judiciously, but it is a valuable addition to salads and also as a potherb, but sparingly. It needs a rich soil and much water.

TARRAGON: (*Artemisia dracunculus*). It dies to the ground in winter, as do many true herbs, but is a very hardy perennial, and the summer growth erects the plant to about two feet high, at which time the small, narrow leaves are at their best for use. Successive cuttings are possible. There are several varieties of Tarragon. The best is French Tarragon. It is best propagated from cuttings or root sections. The seeds on the market are very inferior.

GARDEN THYME: (*Thymus vulgaris*). This hardy perennial herb can be grown from seed. It is better to start with yearling plants, however, because the first year seedlings are hardly large enough for a good crop. Thyme is a favorite herb with experienced cooks, but it should be used sparingly. It is especially good with soups, meat stews, stuffing mixtures, sea-food chowders and a little in salads. It has an interesting history for its medicinal properties. John Gerard, a surgeon in London, in 1597 recommended thyme for stomach ailments. He also said, "Thyme, with honey, is good against the cough and ye shortness of breath." Oil of Thyme was recommended to relieve toothache, in the old English days.

FENNEL, SWEET: (*Foeniculum dulce*). This delicate annual herb should be grown only in the months that are frost free. A native of the Mediterranean countries, it is a favorite herb much used in Italian cooking. In growth-pattern, the stalks are thick, wide, and stocky. If they are

217

banked up with earth, the blanched stems can be cooked as a vegetable—a potherb. Fennel is most noted as a "fish-herb" but it is used as a green canape and a general flavoring agent as well. In ancient Greece, according to the early Greek herbalist, Dioscorides, it was reputed to be an excellent remedy for stomach and bladder troubles. He also wrote, "Juice of the bruised stalks, and ye leaves being dried in ye sun" made a good eye medicine.

TANSY: (*Tanacetum vulgare*). A very hardy perennial, imported from Europe by early colonists Tansy has spread, particularly in the Eastern U.S. until it is almost like a roadside weed. The colonists had many uses for it, notably in puddings, cakes, and teas. In early days it was reputed to be good for stomach troubles and it also was used as a vermifuge and "strewing" herb. William Coles wrote, in 1657, "I have heard that if Maids will take wild tansy and lay it to sod in Buttermilke for the space of nine days, and wash their faces therewith, it will make them look very faire."

FEVERFEW: (*Chrysanthemum parthenium*) This herb is a perennial, able to withstand cold weather also. It is a free self-seeder. When new plants are well started, they should be spaced about ten inches apart, for proper growth. The mature plants will reach a height of probably one to three feet. It is particularly interesting as an ancient medicinal herb that originated in Europe and the Near East. It has been used for many hundreds of years to relieve nervous headaches, neuralgic pains, and even rheumatic twitches. The treatment recommended in these ancient records was

218

to steep the small flowers in hot water to make a tea. Also the entire plant was used to make a tea that relieved fevers and congestions. Also, a tincture made from this plant was a relief from insect bites.

ELECAMPANE: (*Inula helenium*) This hardy, perennial medicinal herb was imported from Europe by the early colonists. Thoroughly acclimated in America, it has become almost a "native weed," that often grows apparently wild in corn fields. There are several varieties, some tall and some short. The tall ones have tropical-looking foliage and large flowers, up to four inches in diameter, of a yellow or orange color. When planted in a garden, it needs at least two feet of space. It has been revered in the past by herbal doctors. Its roots were used in the treatment of stomach disturbances and heart trouble, and its leaves to help relieve the pains of sciatica. An ancient English recipe (Culpepper, 1653) specifies "fresh roots of elecampane preserved with sugar, or made into a syrup or conserve." The recipe further states that "Roots thus prepared are very effectual to warm a cold windy stomach, or the prickling therein, and stitches in the spleen." These herbs are easily raised from seed, or they may be grown from root division in the spring.

ANGELICA: (*Angelica archangelica*). This hardy biennial herb is reputed to have received its name because of its angelic medicinal properties. The English herbalist, William Coles, in 1657, wrote that it was "Soveraigne against the plague; also good for the heart, and if carried on the person will ward off witches!" Angelica is quite tropical in appearance, with large, separated, or divided leaves. The flowers are greenish white, in big umbels. The stalk, which has a sweet taste, is often candied by confectioners. The leaves, which are bittersweet, may be cooked with rhubarb in pie. Normally a biennial, if it is not allowed to bloom, the plant will last for several years. It is a showy plant for the garden, and should be spaced two feet apart. It needs a damp soil, and likes semishade. It may be propagated by root division of two-year-old plants. An oil made from its roots and seeds is used in flavoring vermouth and other liquors.

CHICORY: (*Cichorium intebus*). This hardy perennial herb was a native of Europe. Imported into America by the early colonists, it quickly became naturalized, and "escaped" from careful garden planting. It is familiar today, particularly in Eastern United States, as a beautiful roadside growth, frequently admired because of the beauty of its light-blue flowers. This herb often grows to a height of six feet. It is both a salad herb and a potherb. Its seeds, roasted, have been and are used as a substitute for coffee. There are certain "Coffee and Chicory" mixtures on the markets today. If planted in the spring, the units should be approximately six inches apart, for best growth.

WORMWOOD: (*Artemisia absinthium*). There are several different plants popularly called WORMWOOD but the species *absinthium* is perhaps the most common and familiar one. It is the herb which furnishes the bitter oil that is the ingredient of the liquor, ABSINTHE, also used in other liquors and appetizers, and this oil is an ingredient in a few medicines, as well. Wormwood is a hardy perennial. It grows to an approximate height of from two to four feet. The leaves are gray-green in color, quite abundant, and the flowers, while comparatively small, are greenish yellow. The reputation of WORMWOOD has persisted for many centuries in its native South European habitat as a valuable medicinal herb, particularly for disturbances of stomach and spleen. It is also used as a vermifuge. This true herb dies down to the roots in the fall, but revives in the spring. It is easy to raise it, either from seeds or from cuttings.

ANOTHER VARIETY OF WORMWOOD (*Artemisia pontifica*) is worthy of mention. It also is a hardy perennial. It has been called ROMAN WORMWOOD, with somewhat different leaves. This herb has feathery, silver leaves, and it is a little smaller than the "absinthium," although the properties and uses are similar. ROMAN WORMWOOD was said by Dioscorides, (ancient Greek herbalist), to be a moth repellent, and an excellent remedy for "healing ye bites of ye shrew mouse!" It was also recommended for use with wine, to counteract the effects of poison hemlock. Plants in the garden should be spaced about fifteen inches apart, for proper growth.

WHITE YARROW: (*Achillea millefolium*) is familiar to many, as a fragrant wild flower common along roadsides. It is common in Europe and in Asiatic lands as well as America. It spreads too rapidly and prolifically for a garden, but it is interesting as a medicinal herb, that has been used for bladder troubles, sores of various kinds, and for similar ailments. There is another variety of the same herb, that has red flowers instead of white, that shows the same properties, but is not so spreading, and this red variety makes an excellent garden plant. It is showy, with crimson, rosy flowers, and "Thousand-leafed" (millefolium) gray foliage.

There is a very interesting herb that has a practical, modern use in the weaving and dyeing industry, but which also has had a vital place in mystical history, particularly in ancient Britain and Gaul. A member of the Brassicaceae, The Mustard Family, it is a hardy biennial of quite striking appearance. Because of its renown in the ritualistic practices of the early inhabitants of northern and central Europe, especially among the Druids, it has been given the title, "Honorable." So let it be known as THE HONORABLE WOAD!

WOAD: (*Isatis tinctoria*) needs good rich soil for best results. The first season's growth results in a mass of intensely blue-green lance-shaped leaves that are shiny with a mysterious "aliveness." In early spring of the second season, blue-green thick stems grow up as high as four feet and produce a broad panicle of hundreds of yellow flowers, the effect resembling a huge shallow filigree of delicate lace. When these flowers fade and die, a mass of brown seeds appears, which, if left to mature, will self sow. It is the leaves of this herb that produce the valuable blue dye. This was mentioned in Chapter Three, MYSTERIOUS STONEHENGE, in the discussion of Druidic ritualistic rites. During the Middle Ages in Europe, the commercial culture of WOAD was so important that it was taxed and regulated by governmental decree. Today it is used in the manufacture of blue dyes and as a mordant in the use of indigo. Despite the fact that it is not a food, it will make an attractive addition to any herb garden. Several plants, spaced perhaps six inches apart, will make a good showing.

VALERIAN: (*Valeriana officinalis*) A hardy perennial, has rootstalks that have medicinal properties. Its leaves are used to flavor tobacco. The flowers are very fragrant, and a beautiful pink color. It has been called "Garden Heliotrope."

MANDRAKE: (*Atropa mandragora*) has a long history in legend and romance. It is one of the herbs mentioned in the Bible story of Leah, Rachel, and Jacob. It was thought to have and to confer romantic emotion and fertility powers, as well as its delightful odor and beauty.

The fruits of the true Plant, which is often given the botanical name, *Madragora officinarum,* when ripe, resemble a small tomato, with a pale orange to reddish color, which have a delightful perfume that was mentioned in the Bible, in the story of Solomon.

Mandrake roots, in Roman days, according to Pliny, were said to have the property of anaesthesia. A piece of the root was given to a patient to be chewed during an operation. In those ancient times the Mandrake plant was thought to be excellent to provide restful sleep, to ease pain, to be an aid in cases of mild insanity.

In early England and among the Druids, it was treasured

223

as quite efficacious in combating evil spirits and demons. Today, the leaves are sometimes used in manufacturing external ointments, and its roots have apparent emetic properties. It can be propagated best by root division in the spring.

Another sweet herb mentioned in the Bible (Mark 14:5,6.) is SPIKENARD: (*Nardostachys jatamansi*). This perennial is a native of Nepal and Tibet. In the Song of Solomon, in the Old Testament, it is related, that "While the King sitteth at his table, my SPIKENARD sendeth forth the smell thereof." In ancient times, the fragrant ointment from this small herb was very precious, expensive, and highly prized. Even today, it still is transported in alabaster boxes, on camel back, from the Tibet region where it is still grown. In color, the ointment is a rich rose red, and the odor is "out of this world."

The American variety of this herb is called ARALEA. The botanical name is *Aralea racemosa*. However, it has not yet produced the wonderful properties of the true SPIKENARD. An experiment in plant breeding is suggested, which should prove interesting, indeed.

The following quotation is taken from a book published in 1779, THE TOILET OF FLORA. The author is unknown.

"The Vinegar Of The Four Thieves: Take the tops of Sea and Roman Wormwood, Rosemary, Sage, Mint and Rue, each an ounce and a half; of Lavender flowers two ounces; of Calamus aromaticus, Cinnamon, Cloves, Nutmeg, and

Garlic, of each a quarter of an ounce; of Camphire, half an ounce; of Red Wine Vinegar, a gallon."

This concoction was reputed to be so powerful that it would protect the thieves who were robbing the dead bodies of Plague victims, and render them immune to contagion of the dread disease! It shows quite dramatically the widespread belief in the efficacy of herbs, even in the underworld in the early days. Times have indeed changed. Many of those ancient beliefs are considered to be mere superstitions, in the light of modern scientific knowledge. However, all thinking people will realize that in recent years many things that were formerly considered fanciful dreams have become accepted facts. Space travel is one example. The marvels of electronics also demonstrate the truth that science is an orderly, systematic pursuit of knowledge. Modern medicine owes much of its success to the adaptations of ancient herbal healing lore. In every phase of life, herbs and herbal products are vital.

Truly, modern civilization owes its very existence to the not-so-lowly herb. In order to progress mentally, health is required. Physical and mental health depend on nourishment which means food and the prevention and treatment of disease. The greater portion of our food is derived from herbs and herbal products, and most of our medicines have been developed by observation of the healing principles of Nature.

Explanatory

THE ROSICRUCIAN ORDER

ANTICIPATING questions which may be asked by the readers of this book, the publishers wish to announce that there is but one universal Rosicrucian Order existing in the world today, united in its various jurisdictions, and having one Supreme Council in accordance with the original plan of the ancient Rosicrucian manifestoes. The Rosicrucian Order is not a religious or sectarian society.

This international organization retains the ancient traditions, teachings, principles, and practical helpfulness of the Brotherhood as founded centuries ago. It is known as the *Ancient Mystical Order Rosae Crucis,* which name, for popular use, is abbreviated into AMORC. The Headquarters of the Worldwide Jurisdiction (The Americas, Australasia, Europe, Africa, and Asia) are located at San Jose, California.

Those interested in knowing more of the history and present-day helpful offerings of the Rosicrucians may have a *free* copy of the book entitled, *The Mastery of Life,* by sending a definite request to SCRIBE H.T.T., Rosicrucian Park, San Jose, California 95191.

The Rosicrucian Library

consists of a number of unique books which are
described in the following pages, and which may be
purchased from the
ROSICRUCIAN SUPPLY BUREAU
SAN JOSE, CALIFORNIA 95191, U.S.A.

A THOUSAND YEARS OF YESTERDAYS

by H. Spencer Lewis, F.R.C., Ph.D.

This fascinating story dramatically presents the real facts of reincarnation. It explains how the soul leaves the body and *when* and *why* it returns to Earth again.

This revelation of the *mystic laws and principles* of the Masters of the East has never before been presented in such a form. Finely bound, and stamped in gold, it makes a fine addition to your library.

HERBALISM THROUGH THE AGES

by Ralph Whiteside Kerr, F.R.C.

The seemingly magical power of herbs endowed them with a divine essence to the mind of early man. Not only did they provide some of his earliest foods and become medicines for his illnesses but they also symbolized certain of his emotions and psychic feelings. This book presents the romantic history of herbs and their use even today.

EGYPT'S ANCIENT HERITAGE

by Rodman R. Clayson

Much of what we know today began in Egypt! Concepts that are unquestionably ancient show marvelous insights into natural law. From Egypt's mystery schools came rites and ceremonies that dramatize the creative Cosmic force. This book presents a masterly overview of the civilization of the Nile Valley.

ESSAYS OF A MODERN MYSTIC

by H. Spencer Lewis, F.R.C., Ph. D.

These private writings disclose the personal confidence and enlightenment that are born of *inner experience*. As a true mystic-philosopher, Dr. Lewis shares with his readers the results of contact with the Cosmic intelligence residing within.

MYSTICS AT PRAYER

Compiled by Many Cihlar

The first compilation of the famous prayers of the renowned mystics and adepts of all ages.

The book *Mystics at Prayer* explains in simple language the reason for prayer, how to pray, and the Cosmic laws involved. You come to learn the real efficacy of prayer and its full beauty dawns upon you. Whatever your religious beliefs, this book makes your prayers the application not of words, but of helpful, divine principles. You will learn the infinite power of prayer. Prayer is man's rightful heritage. It is the direct means of man's rightful heritage. It is the direct means of man's communion with the infinite force of divinity.

SELF MASTERY AND FATE WITH THE CYCLES OF LIFE

by H. Spencer Lewis, F.R.C., Ph. D.

This book demonstrates how to harmonize the self with the cyclic forces of each life.

Happiness, health and prosperity are available for those who know the periods in their own life that enhance the success of varying activities. Eliminate "chance" and "luck," cast aside "fate" and replace these with self mastery. Complete with diagrams and lists of cycles.

THE TECHNIQUE OF THE MASTER THE WAY OF COSMIC PREPARATION

by Raymund Andrea, F.R.C.

A guide to inner unfoldment! The newest and simplest explanation for attaining the state of Cosmic Consciousness. To those who have felt the throb of a vital power within, and whose inner vision has at times glimpsed infinite peace and happiness, this book is offered. It converts the intangible whispers of self into forceful actions that bring real joys and accomplishments in life. It is a masterful work on psychic unfoldment.

THE SYMBOLIC PROPHECY OF
THE GREAT PYRAMID

by H. Spencer Lewis, F.R.C., Ph. D.

The world's greatest mystery and first wonder is the Great Pyramid. Its history, vast wisdom and prophecies are all revealed in this beautifully bound and illustrated book. You will be amazed at the pyramid's scientific construction and at the secret knowledge of its mysterious builders.

LEMURIA—THE LOST CONTINENT
OF THE PACIFIC

by Wishar S. Cervé

Where the Pacific now rolls in a majestic sweep for two thousand miles, there was once a vast continent known as Lemuria.

The scientific evidences of this lost race and its astounding civilization with the story of the descendants of the survivors present a cyclical viewpoint of rise and fall in the progress of civilization.

SON OF THE SUN

by Savitri Devi

The amazing story of Akhnaton (Amenhotep IV), Pharaoh of Egypt 1360 B.C. This is not just the fascinating story of one life—it is far more. It raises the curtain on man's emerging from superstition and idolatry. Against the tremendous opposition of a fanatical priesthood, Akhnaton brought about the world's first spiritual revolution. He was the first one to declare that there was a "sole God." In the words of Sir Flinders Petrie (*History of Egypt*): "Were it invented to satisfy our modern scientific conceptions, his religio-philosophy could not be logically improved upon at the present day."

This book contains over three hundred pages. It is handsomely printed, well bound, and stamped in gold.

THE MYSTICAL LIFE OF JESUS

by H. Spencer Lewis, F.R.C., Ph. D.

A full account of Jesus' life, containing the story of his activities in the periods not mentioned in the Gospel accounts, *reveals the real Jesus* at last.

This book required a visit to Palestine and Egypt to secure verification of the strange facts found in Rosicrucian records. Its revelations, predating the discovery of the Dead Sea Scrolls, show aspects of the Essenes unavailable elsewhere.

This volume contains many mystical symbols (fully explained), photographs, and an unusual portrait of Jesus.

THE SECRET DOCTRINES OF JESUS

by H. Spencer Lewis, F.R.C., Ph. D.

Even though the sacred writings of the Bible have had their contents scrutinized, judged and segments removed by twenty ecclesiastical councils since the year 328 A.D., there still remain buried in unexplained passages and parables the Great Master's *personal* doctrines.

Every thinking man and woman will find *hidden truths* in this book.

SEPHER YEZIRAH—A BOOK ON CREATION OR THE JEWISH METAPHYSICS OF REMOTE ANTIQUITY

by Dr. Isidor Kalisch, Translator

The ancient basis for Kabalistic thought is revealed in this outstanding metaphysical essay concerning all creation. It explains the secret name of Jehovah.

Containing both the Hebrew and English texts, its 61 pages have been photolithographed from the 1877 edition. As an added convenience to students of Kabala, it contains a glossary of the original Hebraic words and terms.

MENTAL POISONING
THOUGHTS THAT ENSLAVE MINDS

by H. Spencer Lewis, F.R.C. Ph. D.

Must humanity remain at the mercy of evil influences created in the minds of the vicious? Do poisoned thoughts find innocent victims? Use the knowledge this book fearlessly presents as an antidote for such superstitions and their influences.

There is no need to remain helpless even though evil thoughts of envy, hate, and jealousy are aimed to destroy your self-confidence and peace of mind.

BEHOLD THE SIGN

by Ralph M. Lewis, F.R.C.

Unwrap the veil of mystery from the strange symbols inherited from antiquity. What were the *Sacred Traditions* said to be revealed to Moses? What were the discoveries of the Egyptian priesthood?

This book is fully illustrated with *age-old secret symbols* whose true meanings are often misunderstood. Even the mystical beginnings of the *secret signs* of many fraternal brotherhoods today are explained.

THE TECHNIQUE OF THE DISCIPLE

by Raymund Andrea, F.R.C.

The Technique of the Disciple is a book containing a modern description of the ancient esoteric path to spiritual Illumination, trod by the masters and avatars of yore. It has long been said that Christ left, as a great heritage to members of His secret council, a private method for guidance in life, which method has been preserved until today in the secret, occult, mystery schools.

Raymund Andrea, the author, reveals the method for attaining a greater life taught in these mystery schools, which perhaps parallels the secret instructions of Christ to members of His council. The book is informative, inspiring, and splendidly written. It is handsomely bound stamped in gold.

"UNTO THEE I GRANT..."

as revised by Sri Ramatherio

Out of the mysteries of the past comes this antique book that was written two thousand years ago, but was hidden in manuscript form from the eyes of the world and given only to the initiates of the temples in Tibet to study privately.

It can be compared only with the writings attributed to Solomon in the Bible of today. It deals with man's passions, weaknesses, fortitudes and hopes. Included is the story of the expedition into Tibet that secured the manuscript and the Grand Lama's permission to translate it.

————

THE BOOK OF JASHER
THE SACRED BOOK WITHHELD

What was written in this book of Holy Scripture that caused it to be expunged from the pages of the Bible? To what *veiled truths* were the prophets of old referring when they cried, "Is it not written in the Book of Jasher?"—Joshua 10:13, "Behold, it is written in the Book of Jasher" —II Samuel 1:18?

Read this photographic reproduction of the text whose rediscovery is credited to Alcuin, sage of Charlemagne's court.

————

COSMIC MISSION FULFILLED

by Ralph M. Lewis, F.R.C.

This illustrated biography of Harvey Spencer Lewis, Imperator of the Ancient, Mystical Order Rosae Crucis, was written in response to the requests of thousands of members who sought the key to this mystic-philosopher's life mission of rekindling the ancient flame of *Wisdom* in the Western world. We view his triumphs and tribulations from the viewpoint of those who knew him best.

Recognize, like him, that the present is our *moment in Eternity*; in it we fulfill our mission.

CONSCIOUS INTERLUDE

by Ralph M. Lewis, F.R.C.

With clarity of expression and insightful penetration of thought, this original philosopher leads us to contemplate such subjects as: the Fourth Dimension, the Mysteries of Time and Space; the Illusions of Law and Order; and many others of similar import.

As you follow the author through the pages into broad universal concepts, your mind too will feel its release into an expanding consciousness.

WHISPERINGS OF SELF

by Validivar

Wisdom, wit and insight combine in these brief aphorisms that derive from the interpretation of Cosmic impulses received by Validivar, whose true name is Ralph M. Lewis, Imperator of the Rosicrucian Order.

These viewpoints of all areas of human experience make an attractive gift as well as a treasured possession of your own.

ETERNAL FRUITS OF KNOWLEDGE

by Cecil A. Poole, F.R.C.

A stimulating presentation of philosophical insights that will provoke you into considering new aspects of such questions as: the purpose of human existence, the value of mysticism, and the true nature of good and evil. Paperback.

CARES THAT INFEST...

by Cecil A. Poole, F.R.C.

With a penetrating clarity, Cecil Poole presents us with the key to understanding our problems so that we may open wide the door and dismiss care from our lives. The author guides us on a search for *true value* so that, in the poet's words, "the night will be filled with music," as the *cares* "silently steal away."

ROSICRUCIAN MANUAL
by H. Spencer Lewis, F.R.C., Ph. D.

This practical book contains not only extracts from the Constitution of the Rosicrucian Order, but a complete outline and explanation of all the customs, habits, and terminology of the Rosicrucians, with diagrams and explanations of the symbols used in the teachings, an outline of the subjects taught, a dictionary of the terms, a complete presentation of the principles of Cosmic Consciousness, and biographical sketches of important individuals connected with the work. There are also special articles on the Great White Lodge and its existence, how to attain psychic illumination, the Rosicrucian Code of Life with twenty-nine laws and regulations, and a number of portraits of prominent mystics including Master K. H., the Illustrious.

The technical matter in the text and in the numerous diagrams makes this book a real encyclopedia of Rosicrucian explanations, aside from the dictionary of Rosicrucian terms.

The *Rosicrucian Manual* has been enlarged and improved since its first edition. Attractively bound, and stamped in gold.

MESSAGES FROM THE CELESTIAL SANCTUM
by Raymond Bernard, F.R.C.

The real *unity* is Cosmic Unity. No human being is separated from the Cosmic, no matter where he lives or how different his life style may be. Each person is like a channel through which cosmically inspired intuitive impressions and guidance can flow. The *Celestial Sanctum* in general is the universe. No earthly sanctuary is more sacred than the multiple phenomena which occur in the great extensions of the Cosmic. There are no greater Laws than those which operate this phenomenon.

This book explains how you can harmonize yourself with the *Celestial Sanctum*. Also, it reveals rational, sensible, and practical messages which were *cosmically* narrated. They can guide all, regardless of race or creed, toward a greater understanding and a complete mastery of one's life. Allow this book to explain to you how your mind can become like a window through which you can observe creation—and learn from it in a *personal way*.

MANSIONS OF THE SOUL
by H. Spencer Lewis, F.R.C., Ph. D.

Reincarnation: the world's most disputed doctrine! What did Jesus mean when he referred to the mansions in my Father's house? This book demonstrates what Jesus and his immediate followers knew about the rebirth of the soul, as well as what has been taught by sacred works and scholarly authorities in all parts of the world.

Learn about the cycles of the soul's reincarnations and how you can become acquainted with your present self and your past lives.

THE SANCTUARY OF SELF
by Ralph M. Lewis, F.R.C.

Are you living your life to your best advantage? Are you beset by a *conflict of desires?* Do you know that there are various *loves* and that some of them are dangerous drives?

Learn which of your feelings to discard as enslaving influences and which to retain as worthy incentives.

The author, Imperator of the Rosicrucian Order, brings to you from his years of experience, the practical aspects of mysticism.

ROSICRUCIAN PRINCIPLES FOR THE HOME AND BUSINESS
by H. Spencer Lewis, F.R.C., Ph. D.

This volume contains the practical application of Rosicrucian teachings to such problems as: ill health, common ailments, how to increase one's income or promote business propositions. It shows not only what to do, but what to avoid, in using metaphysical and mystical principles in starting and bringing into realization new plans and ideas.

Both business organizations and business authorities have endorsed this book.

ROSICRUCIAN QUESTIONS AND ANSWERS WITH COMPLETE HISTORY OF THE ORDER

by H. Spencer Lewis, F.R.C. Ph. D.

From ancient times to the present day, the history of the Rosicrucian Order is traced from its earliest traditional beginnings. Its historical facts are illuminated by stories of romance and mystery.

Hundreds of questions in this well-indexed volume are answered, dealing with the work, benefits and purposes of the Order.

———

MYSTICISM—THE ULTIMATE EXPERIENCE

by Cecil A. Poole, F.R.C.

An experience is more than just a sensation, a feeling. It is an *awareness,* or perception, with *meaning.* Our experiences are infinite in number, yet they are limited to certain types. Some are related to our objective senses; others, to dreams and inspirational ideas. But there is *one* that transcends them all—the *mystical experience.* It serves every category of our being: it stimulates, it enlightens, it strengthens; it is the *Ultimate Experience.*

And this book, *Mysticism—The Ultimate Experience,* defines it in simple and inspiring terms.

———

IN SEARCH OF REALITY

by Cecil A. Poole, F.R.C.

This Book Unites Metaphysics With Mysticism.

Man is not just an isolated entity on Earth. He is also of a great world—the Cosmos. The forces that create galaxies and island universes also flow through man's being. The human body and its vital phenomenon—Life—are of the same spectrum of energy of which all creation consists. The universe is you because you are one of its myriad forms of existence. Stripping away the mystery of this Cosmic relationship increases the personal reality of the Self.

YESTERDAY HAS MUCH TO TELL

by Ralph M. Lewis, F.R.C.

A personal account of witnessing primitive ceremonies, conversations with mystical teachers and austere high priests of the Near and Far East. It takes you to rites in the interior of Africa, and to temples in Peru, India, Egypt and other exotic lands. This is no mere travel book; the author was privileged, because of his Rosicrucian affiliation, to see and learn that which is not ordinarily revealed.

MENTAL ALCHEMY

by Ralph M. Lewis, F.R.C.

We can transmute our problems to workable solutions through *mental alchemy*. While this process is neither easy nor instantaneously effective, eventually the serious person will be rewarded. Certain aspects of our lives *can* be altered to make them more compatible with our goals.

Use this book to alter the direction of your life through proper thought and an understanding of practical mystical philosophy.

THROUGH THE MIND'S EYE

by Ralph M. Lewis, F.R.C.

Truth Is What Is Real To Us. Knowledge, experience, is the material of which truth consists. But what is the *real, the true,* of what we know? With expanding consciousness and knowledge, truth changes. Truth therefore is ever in the *balance*—never the same. But in turning to important challenging subjects, the *Mind's Eye* can extract that which is the true and the real, for the *now*. The book, *Through The Mind's Eye,* calls to attention important topics for judgment by your mind's eye.

THE CONSCIENCE OF SCIENCE
and Other Essays

by Walter J. Albersheim, Sc.D., F.R.C.

A remarkable collection of fifty-four essays by one of the most forthright writers in the field of science and mysticism. His frank and outspoken manner will challenge readers to look again to their own inner light, as it were, to cope with the ponderous advances in modern technology.
